The Secret

Of Handling Money God's Way
for ages 8 – 12

Luke

Rosie

Bethany

Nathan

CROWN FINANCIAL MINISTRIES®
biblical financial freedom

This book was written by Jenny Poole and illustrated by Abigail Suckling

Contents

Welcome

You are about to start the exciting journey of discovering God's secret of handling money

Today you may be handling a small amount of money. Maybe you have some pocket money or even receive money from doing jobs. You may receive money as an alternative to gifts for your birthday or at Christmas. Some children save their money – others spend it quickly while some spend, save and give. The twelve chapters of this book tell a story, but you will discover in the story some important principles about how to handle money.

These truths apply today, but will also apply in your teenage years – and beyond. You will find that these truths are found in the Bible, a book that includes a lot about how we should handle our money. These principles work so enjoy our story and learning about what the Bible has to teach us all.

Studying with a group?

This book can be used for group study. Each child will need their own copy and a teachers guide is available containing directions for group use together with activities, quizzes and puzzles.

Copyright © 2010 by Crown Financial Ministries, Inc.

All rights reserved

Published by Crown Financial Ministries UK

Photocopying or any other form of duplication is strictly prohibited

Illustrated by Abigail Suckling

Typesetting and layout design by Fleur Isbell

Unless otherwise noted, Scripture quotations are from the Holy Bible: New International Version – UK, Copyright © 1973, 1978, 1984 by the International Bible Society.

Verses identified as NASB are taken from the New American Standard Bible, Copyright © 1960, 1962, 1963, 1968, 1971, 1972, 1973, 1975, 1977, 1995 by the Lockman Foundation.

Verses identified as NLT are taken from the Holy Bible: New Living Translation, Copyright © 1996, 2004 by Tyndale Charitable Trust. Used by permission of Tyndale House Publishers.

Verses identified as AMP are taken from the Amplified Bible, Copyright © 1954, 1958, 1962, 1964, 1965, 1987 by the Lockman Foundation.

Verses identified as KJV are taken from the King James Version of the Bible: Public Domain.

ISBN: 978-0-9560093-7-1

Printed in the United Kingdom

This book belongs to:

_____

About this book

At the end of each chapter you will have the opportunity to do some fun things that will help you learn and apply good money principles. Here they are:

Memorise a verse

The best way to remember God's truth is to memorise it. So you will memorise one special verse at the end of each chapter.

Answer these questions

You will think about and write down your answers to some great questions.

Work it out

Next you will do something that will really help you with your money – like opening a savings account.

Write your prayer here

At the end of each chapter write out and speak your prayer to God and watch for His answer.

For group use

Now, this will be exciting! You can write down what other people want you to pray about for them, and they will write down your prayer requests. Use the prayer record on page 94. Then you will pray for each other every day – and watch God answer your prayers.

chapter 1

The start of it all

It was a warm Friday afternoon at the start of April and the pupils of the Year Six Class at Greenwood School were waiting to hear the school bell and head for home. Nathan glanced across at his friend, Luke.

"Are you still up for our plan this weekend?" he whispered.

"Can't wait!" Luke nodded.

The boys had decided to make a den and had thought about little else all week. But suddenly their attention was caught by an announcement from their teacher, Mr Lewis.

"One more thing before you go," he said with a smile. "In July the school is running an activity holiday in the Welsh mountains. It will be a great week and we would like as many of you to come as possible. You'll have the chance to try out lots of activities – canoeing, rock climbing, abseiling, raft building and much more. The details are in this letter for your parents. The money needs to be in the week before the holiday, which gives you more than three months to save up."

Mr Lewis started to hand the letters out as the bell rang for home time. Nathan turned to Luke. "Wow! That sounds amazing!"

"You can say that again!" said a voice behind them, as Bethany and her friend Rosie walked out of the class with the boys. "Canoeing...I've always wanted to try that."

"Yes," agreed Rosie, pointing to the letter. "And look, it says we'll be learning map reading and orienteering *and* spending a day at the sea."

"I wonder if we'll get to do body boarding," exclaimed Nathan excitedly. "You'd love that Luke!"

"Yes, I would," said Luke in such a fed-up voice that the others looked at him in surprise. "Well, I'm not going to be able to go, am I?" he said in response to them. My mum's on her own and there's no way she could pay for this. She struggles just to buy food and clothes for me, Jess and Olivia. There's no point me getting excited."

"Oh, I hadn't thought about the cost," Rosie also looked subdued. "It *is* a lot of money. I don't know if mum and dad could pay for me, especially since the new baby arrived."

"And my parents are saving all their money for when Ben starts university in September," said Nathan. "At least you'll be OK Bethany. Your parents have loads of money!"

"But it'll be no fun going without the rest of you," sighed Bethany.

The four friends walked along in silence, their excitement gone. Then Nathan grabbed Luke's arm. "I've got an idea! Why don't we find a way to earn enough money to pay for the holiday?"

"How are we going to do that?" Luke asked gloomily. "What can four eleven-year-old kids do to earn all that money?"

"I know," said Nathan. "We'll ask my brother, Ben. He's been learning about money on some course at church and saving, ready for university. Maybe he'll have some good ideas."

"It's worth a try," agreed Rosie. "Shall we all come to your house tomorrow morning?"

"That'll be great," said Nathan. "See you then!"

Bethany was deep in thought as she opened her front door. She really hoped her friends could find some way of getting the money. Both of her parents were doctors and she was their only daughter, so she had never had to think about money before. Her mum was waiting for her in the kitchen.

"Hi sweetheart. Have you had a good day at school?"

Bethany nodded as she handed her mum the letter.

"My friends don't think they can afford to go," she said, taking some juice from the fridge. "I know you can pay for me but it won't be so much fun without them. They're trying to find a way to earn some money."

Mrs Kasanga looked thoughtful. "You are right, dear. We could pay for you to go. But I think you're old enough to start learning the value of money, and this will be a good time for you to earn the money yourself too."

"But mum!" Bethany put her glass down with a thud. "That's not fair!"

"I think you'll appreciate the holiday far more if you've worked for it yourself, just like your friends. Your father and I want you to be wise about money, and not think there is an endless supply coming from us. This sounds like a good time to start."

"We're meeting at Nathan's tomorrow," said Bethany, still a little put-out. "Ben might have some good ideas."

"That sounds great," said Mrs Kasanga, giving her daughter a hug. "Let us know how you get on."

* * * *

The four friends met at Nathan's early the following morning. Nathan, Luke and Rosie were surprised to hear Bethany's news.

"At least it means we're all in this together," said Rosie.

Bethany nodded, looking a bit more cheerful. Then she laughed as a big golden retriever jumped up at her, pushing her onto the settee and licking her face.

"Hello, Minty. You're always pleased to see me, aren't you?"

"That's because you fuss her,"

smiled Nathan. "She's a big softie, this one. It's only a couple of weeks now 'til her puppies are due to be born."

"Make sure you let us know straight away," Bethany stroked Minty's head. "I can't wait to see them."

Nathan nodded then jumped up as the door opened and Ben walked into the lounge. He looked like a taller version of Nathan, with the same dark hair and friendly smile.

"Hi all of you," Ben greeted them. "Nathan tells me you need to raise some money."

"The holiday sounds so amazing," Rosie told him. "But none of our parents can pay for us to go. Nathan thought you could help us think of ways to earn the money."

"We'd do anything to go," Luke added. "We just don't know what to do."

Ben looked at them all. "I know a good place for you to start finding out about money," he said.

"Where?" they asked in unison.

"Right here," Ben said, picking up a book from the table. "This book has the answers to a lot of my problems."

"That's the Bible," exclaimed Nathan.

"What can *that* tell us about earning money to go on holiday?" asked Luke, suspiciously. He had a lot of respect for Ben but was not too sure about the Bible.

Ben smiled and sat down between Luke and Rosie. "I've been doing a course at church studying what the Bible says about money, and believe me it says a lot. Did you know there are 2,350 verses in the Bible that talk about how we handle money?"

*   *   *   *

Rosie was growing impatient. "But Ben, we need to know how to earn money," she said. "If we don't, we'll never make it on this holiday."

"I understand, Rosie," Ben answered. "I'll make a deal with you. If you let me teach you some of the things that God says about the way we should handle money, then I will help you find some ways to earn enough money for the holiday. There will be twelve lessons. Before each lesson you'll need to look up some Bible verses and answer questions. You'll also memorise a

Bible verse for each lesson."

Luke was not convinced. "I don't even have a Bible."

"Nor me," echoed Rosie.

"I've got one you can have, Luke," offered Nathan.

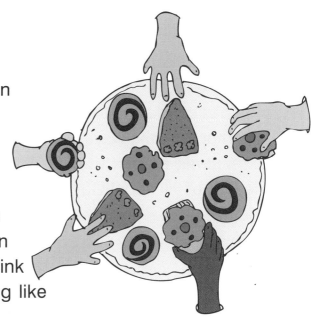

"And I'm sure we've got a spare one at home for you, Rosie," chimed in Bethany. "It does sound interesting. I think my mum and dad have done something like this at church too."

"It's helped me to get ready for university more than anything else," said Ben. "And if you keep your part of the deal, you can help me sort the garden for dad."

"The jungle, you mean!" Nathan interrupted with a chuckle.

"It is in a bit of a state, isn't it?" Bethany agreed looking out of the window.

"Dad is paying me to clear it over the next couple of months," Ben explained. "If you all help, I'll share the money with you. It would be a start anyway."

"Will you really?" Rosie said. "It would be so exciting if we could go to Wales."

"Is it a deal, then?" Ben asked, standing up and pushing Minty off his feet, where she had been lying since he sat down.

"Yeah, it's a deal!" said Luke, and the others nodded, looking excited for the first time.

*   *   *   *

The door opened and Nathan's mum came in. "Anyone want juice and cake?" she asked.

"Yes please!" they all exclaimed, and then Bethany turned to Ben.

"Can we start right now on our first lesson?" she asked.

"I don't see why not," said Ben, taking the plate of cake from Mrs Howard. "Thanks mum. These look great." He offered them around to the others, then laughed as Minty settled down on the floor, with her head on Bethany's lap.

"Looks like Minty wants to listen too!" Luke commented.

"Here we go then," said Ben. "There are three things you need to remember from this lesson. The first is that God says a lot about how we should handle money. Remember, there are 2,350 verses in the Bible that talk about money. Why do you think God said so much about money? He wanted to give us clear directions for how to use it. He wanted to help us avoid making mistakes in handling it."

"The second thing to remember is that God's way for us to handle money is different from the way most people handle it. God tells us in *Isaiah 55:8-9: "My thoughts are not your thoughts, neither are your ways My ways."* The Bible tells us all about God's ways, and that includes how we should handle money."

"We'll be able to remember that, Ben," said Rosie. "What else do we need to know?"

Ben picked up the Bible and turned to *Luke 16:11*. "Nathan, can you read this for us?"

Nathan took the Bible. *"Therefore if you have not been faithful in the use of worldly wealth, who will entrust the true riches to you?" (NASB)*

"That's a bit harder to understand," said Ben. "But it means: if you handle your money the way God wants you to, you'll become closer friends with God. The great benefits of knowing Him well are the 'true riches' mentioned in that verse."

"Come over next Sunday afternoon and we'll look at the second lesson," Ben said. "It's about what part God plays with our money. Oh, and before you go, I'll make a list of the verses for you to look up and the questions for you to answer."

"Don't forget the verses to memorise," Bethany reminded him.

"Those too!" Ben smiled at her. "Just think, in three months you'll be handing that money in and getting ready to go on holiday! It actually sounds a lot of fun…for a school holiday! Do you think ex-pupils would be allowed?"

The first lesson ended in uproar as the children jumped on Ben and wrestled him to the floor, Minty running between them and barking excitedly at the noise.

Memorise a verse

Therefore if you have not been faithful in the use of worldly wealth, who will entrust the true riches to you? (Luke 16:11, NASB)

Answer these questions

1. There are more than 2,350 verses in the Bible that talk about money. Why do you think the Bible says so much about money?

_____

_____

_____

_____

2. Open the Bible and read *Isaiah 55:8-9*. Do you think God's way of handling money is different from the way most people handle money?

_____

_____

_____

_____

3. What do you think is the greatest difference?

_____

_____

_____

_____

4. Look up and read *Luke 16:11*. What do you think are the 'true riches' the Lord mentions in this verse?

_____

_____

_____

Work it out

If you do not have a Bible, please get one so you can look up what God wants you to know about money. Look at the books of the Bible listed in the front of your Bible – they start with Genesis and end with Revelation. Some of the books are in the Old Testament and some in the New Testament.

Count the books in the Bible. How many are there? _____

Write your prayer here

_____

_____

_____

_____

_____

_____

→ Studying with a group
Get ready for the next chapter

Read chapter 2, memorise _1 Chronicles 29:11-12_ and answer the questions on page15 then complete the _Work It Out_ exercise on page 16.

A giant at the den

"Come on, Rosie, I'll beat you to Nathan's," Luke called as he cycled along the small road leading to Nathan's house.

"Slow down a bit!" Rosie puffed as she caught up with him. "What do you think the surprise is that Nathan told us about?"

Nathan had phoned them both up after lunch telling them to come as soon as they could, as Ben had a surprise for them all.

"I don't think Nathan knows either," Luke answered. "But we'll soon find out, we're here now."

They leaned their bikes next to the front door and were about to ring when Nathan opened the door.

"I thought I heard you arrive," he exclaimed excitedly. "Come on, Ben won't tell us anything 'til you two are here."

Rosie and Luke followed Nathan into the lounge. Bethany was already there, stroking Minty.

"Hi Beth," Rosie greeted her. "How come you're here so soon? We came as soon as Nathan phoned and you live further away."

"Mum and dad and I had lunch with Nathan's family after church," Bethany explained. "Where's Ben gone? Now that we're all here, he's disappeared!"

"Ben!" Nathan called, pushing open the kitchen door, the other three close on his heels.

"Whoa!" Ben chuckled as they all bumped into him. "You four are excited today. What's going on?"

"You know!" Nathan poked him playfully. "Why were you out in the garden so long yesterday?"

"Come on, Ben, don't keep us waiting any longer," pleaded Luke.

"Ok," Ben smiled. "Follow me."

The four children followed Ben out into the garden and down a path which could only just be seen between the overgrown grass and plants. Trees with long, green branches hung over the path.

"Wow, this garden does need some attention!" whistled Luke.

"That's our job in a couple of weeks," Ben reminded them. "Here we are. What do you think?"

He stood back and let the children push past him. There was a wooden shed in front of them. Two sides were against the fence and the third was almost covered by the ivy growing over it. At the front, were two small windows and a door. The shed was old but looked as though some repairs had recently been carried out on it.

"I forgot this shed was here," Nathan exclaimed. "Dad used to store guitars in here when he ran the business, didn't he?"

Ben nodded and handed Rosie a large key. "Unlock it and have a look inside," he said.

Rosie turned the key and pushed open the door. The children crowded around and waited for their eyes to adjust to the dim interior.

The shed was bigger inside than it appeared from the outside. It was dusty, but clear with a few solid-looking boxes to sit on, and even an old mat on the floor.

"Did you clear this out?" Nathan asked his brother. "It's great!"

Ben smiled. "Not bad for a few hours work. I thought it would be good to have a base to do our lessons."

"We wanted to make a den," Luke reminded Nathan.

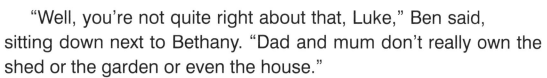

"It's wonderful," said Bethany, sitting on one of the boxes. "Thanks, Ben."

"We can't tell anyone else about it," Rosie announced. "It's our headquarters. It belongs just to us!"

"Not really," said Luke. "It belongs to Mr and Mrs Howard. They're just letting us use it."

"Well, you're not quite right about that, Luke," Ben said, sitting down next to Bethany. "Dad and mum don't really own the shed or the garden or even the house."

"If they don't, then who does?" Nathan questioned.

Ben turned around and pulled his Bible off a small shelf behind him. "I even put this in ready for our lessons," he grinned. "Now let me tell you about the owner of the den."

He opened the Bible and said, "In this lesson I want you to learn what part God plays with our money. There are three things that are important to understand. The first is that the Lord owns everything. Listen to this: *The earth is the Lord's, and everything in it, the world, and all who live in it (Psalm 24:1)."*

"God owns this den," Ben said. "He owns the house, the garden, your houses, your bikes – God even owns us. God owns everything. The Bible lists some of the things that the Lord owns. In *Leviticus 25:23* the Bible tells us He owns the land, and *Haggai 2:8* tells us He owns the silver and gold. *Psalm 50:10-11* says: *"Every animal of the forest is mine, and the cattle on a thousand hills…and the creatures of the field are mine."*

They sat quietly thinking about Ben's words. Suddenly the door creaked and made them all jump. It slowly opened and a golden head peered round at them all.

"Minty!" Rosie laughed. "You made us jump!"

"Hey, Ben," Bethany turned to him. "I suppose that means God owns Minty too?"

"Yes," Ben agreed. "And soon, God will own some puppies as well."

Luke whistled softly and shook his head. "Now I see what you meant when you told us that God's ways are different than ours. We never would have known He was the owner of everything if the Bible hadn't told us."

Ben nodded his head. "Now the second part is really special. God is in ultimate control of everything that happens to you. Knowing the Lord is in control helps us to be at peace when things seem to go wrong. It gives us courage when we are faced with problems."

"Like getting enough money to go on holiday," said Rosie.

Ben smiled. "What you guys are facing reminds me of a story in the Bible about a boy just about your age who dealt with a giant problem."

"You're talking about David, aren't you?" Bethany interrupted.

"Yes, Bethany," Ben answered. "David was just a young boy taking care of his father's sheep. Did you know that he killed both a lion and a bear when they tried to attack the sheep? How would you like to face a hungry bear all by yourself?"

"But he wasn't all by himself," Nathan said. "God was with him!"

"You're right, Nathan," Ben agreed.

"Tell us about the giant," Rosie said.

*   *   *   *

"Ok," Ben answered. "The whole army of Israel was afraid of a giant named Goliath who was nearly 3 metres tall!" Ben stood up and said, "Follow me."

Ben led the four friends outside, where he had piled boxes 3 metres high in the tall grass. "I had to do something with the boxes I cleared out of the shed!" he grinned. "Stand next to them so you can see how big Goliath was."

"Wow!" Luke said with a whistle.

"David's older brothers were soldiers in the army, and David's father sent him to take food to his brothers. When David arrived, he found that everyone was terrified of Goliath."

"Every day for forty days Goliath shouted to the Israelites, 'Choose a man and let us fight each other. If he kills me, we will become your slaves; but if I kill him, you will be our slaves.' But they were so afraid of Goliath that no one would fight him."

"However, David was brave because he knew God was in control, even of Goliath. He remembered how God had taken care of him when he faced a bear and a lion. So he volunteered to fight Goliath. Imagine a young boy fighting a three metre giant!"

"What happened?" Rosie asked, her eyes big with excitement.

"David took a smooth stone and put it in a sling," Ben said as he started to swing an imaginary sling over his head. Then he shouted, "Goliath, you come to fight me with a sword and a spear, but I come in the name of the Lord!" Ben threw the imaginary stone at the Goliath made of boxes.

"The stone struck the giant in the head and he fell over dead. Come on, guys, help me knock over Goliath!" The friends laughed as they ran over to help Ben push the boxes to the ground.

Ben rubbed his hands together to get rid of the dust and grass and continued. "Now, here's the most important part of the story. Listen to what David said many years after he killed that giant. *Everything in the heavens and on earth is yours, O Lord, and this is your kingdom. We adore you as the one who is over all things (1 Chronicles 29:11, NLT)*."

"Even though David had become a great and powerful king, he still knew God was the owner of everything and in control of everything."

Ben stopped and wiped his forehead on his sleeve. "Whew, I forgot how much work it is to tell a story!"

"Especially when you tell *and* show the story!" said a voice behind them with a laugh.

"Susie!" said Nathan, as Ben's girlfriend walked over to them. "How long have you been there?"

"Long enough to learn something new about you, Ben," Susie chuckled. "I didn't know you could tell stories like that!"

Ben looked embarrassed but Bethany grabbed Susie's arm. "Come and see our den," she said pulling her into the shed, and the others followed.

"This is great!" Susie agreed. "Did you do this too, Ben?"

"Yes, he did," Luke answered for him. "This is our headquarters. Ben's helping us raise money for the holiday."

"I know," Susie nodded. "That's why I'm here too, but have you finished your lesson before I explain?"

"No," said Nathan, turning to Ben. "God owns everything, and He controls everything. What else?"

"He promises to meet our needs," Ben replied. "Look out there at those black crows on the fence. They remind me of the ravens that brought bread and meat to Elijah every morning and every evening during a famine."

*   *   *   *

"Elijah was God's prophet. But he found himself in the middle of a famine. There was no food anywhere. But God used ravens to bring food for him every day. God never let him down. And He won't let you down either."

"That's right," Susie agreed. "And God's sent me with part of the answer for you."

"What's that then?" asked Rosie with a puzzled look on her face.

"You know my dad owns Pinewoods Nature Reserve not

far from here" she replied and the children nodded. "Well, he needs some extra help there to get ready for the summer holidays, as that's always our busiest time. How would you four like to earn some money by helping out?"

"Are you serious?" Bethany gasped. "That would be amazing!"

"Brilliant!" Luke agreed. "We'd love to, wouldn't we guys?"

They all nodded and Susie looked pleased. "That's settled then," she said. "I'll tell dad you'll be there next Saturday."

"Then you can come back here for tea and we'll have the next lesson," Ben added.

"Great!" Nathan said, and then jumped up as there was a knock at the door. "More visitors! So much for keeping this place secret!"

The door opened and Bethany's parents looked in.

"So this is where you got to!" Mr Kasanga chuckled. "We thought it was quiet back at the house!"

"Come in, mum and dad," Bethany exclaimed. "And we can tell you what we've been learning."

"I don't think there's room for us in there!" Mrs Kasanga smiled. "We do have something to tell you though."

Her husband nodded. "Ben has been telling us what he is teaching you, and we think it is an excellent idea. God's ways are definitely the best ways to live by. We want to make a deal with you. There's a secret we want you to discover – God's secret of handling money. We'll give you several clues in the next few weeks, and if you can guess the secret before the holiday, we'll pay half of the cost of the holiday for each of you."

"Really!" Rosie exclaimed. "You'd do that for us?"

Mr Kasanga nodded as Bethany gave him a hug.

"Thanks, dad. That's wonderful!"

"What's the first clue?" asked Luke eagerly.

Mr Kasanga smiled. "The first clue is this: when you discover the secret, it will mean even more to you than going on holiday."

The children looked at each other. "This first clue is hard to believe," Nathan voiced what they were all thinking. "What could mean more to us than going on this holiday?"

Memorise a verse

Everything in the heavens and on earth is yours, O Lord, and this is your kingdom. We adore you as the one who is over all things. Wealth and honour come from you alone, for you rule over everything. Power and might are in your hand, and at your discretion people are made great and given strength (1 Chronicles 29:11-12, NLT).

Answer these questions

1. Read *1 Corinthians 10:26*. Who owns everything in the world?

_____

_____

2. Name some of your things that God owns?

_____

_____

3. Read *1 Chronicles 29:11-12*. Who ultimately rules over all things?

_____

_____

4. List some of the things people need to live life daily.

_____

_____

_____

5. Read *Matthew 6:31-33* and *Philippians 4:19*. What do these verses say about God taking care of your needs?

_____

_____

_____

6. Give an example from the Bible of the Lord providing for someone's needs.

_____

_____

_____

7. What was the most interesting thing you have learned from this chapter?

_____

_____

_____

Work it out

The first step in learning to handle money is to know how much money you get and how much you spend. Write down what you receive and spend each week.

Money I receive:
Pocket money _____
Jobs _____
Gifts _____
Other income _____
Total I receive for the week _____

Money I spend:
Giving _____
Entertainment _____
Food _____
Clothes _____
Music _____
Sports _____
Other spending _____
Total I spend in the week _____

Do you spend more money than you receive? ❏ Yes ❏ No

If so, how much more do you spend? _____

Write your prayer here

_____
_____
_____
_____

Studying with a group
Get ready for the next chapter

Read chapter 3, memorise *1 Corinthians 4:2* and answer the questions on page 23 then complete the *Work It Out* exercise on page 24.

Pinewoods

Early on Saturday morning the four friends gathered at the entrance to Pinewoods Nature Reserve with Ben.

"I've been looking forward to this all week!" exclaimed Bethany, who loved animals. "I've visited so many times but working here is really cool!"

"I'll tell you something that's even better," said Luke with a grin. "We're getting paid too!"

Ben chuckled. "It is hard work though. I've been working here for a while and you'll be earning your money today, I can tell you!"

"We're up for the challenge," Nathan said. "Here's Susie and her dad. Come on, let's get started."

Susie's dad welcomed them and led them into the small office behind the entrance.

"Thanks for coming today," he said. "I've got two main jobs for the day. Two of you can help Susie to clean out the animal pens, while the other two can work with Ben to check the fence around the edge of the reserve. I know several places that need repairing. We can't have the animals getting out – or the visitors, for that matter! Who would like to do what?"

"Oh, please can I work with the animals?" Bethany begged.

"Fence for me," said Luke, who was not a huge animal fan.

"I'd like to work outside today," agreed Rosie. "Are you OK with Bethany, Nathan?"

"Yeah, that's fine by me," Nathan nodded.

Mr Brent was pleased. "If you work well this morning, I'll show you around the reserve after lunch," he promised.

Ben, Luke and Rosie headed for the workshop to collect the tools they needed, and Susie turned to Bethany and Nathan.

"Which animals shall we start with?" she asked.

"How about the rabbits and guinea pigs," Bethany suggested.

They set off for the barn where the smaller animals were housed, stopping to get some brushes and buckets of water on the way.

"The animals are used to being around people, but make sure you don't leave the gates open as you're cleaning," Susie instructed.

"We'll be careful," promised Nathan, chuckling as he pictured himself and Bethany chasing rabbits around the yard.

They worked hard and soon the rabbits and guinea pigs were enjoying their clean pens and fresh, sweet-smelling hay. Bethany was thrilled when Susie said she could hold some of the smaller animals.

"This is more like playing than work," she said, as she stroked the black and white rabbit sitting on her lap. "You are fortunate to live here all the time, Susie."

"I suppose I am," Susie told her. "I'm used to it. Dad has owned Pinewoods since I was a lot younger than you."

"Why did he start it?" asked Nathan.

"He's always loved animals," Susie replied. "And he wanted to do something to help children with special needs who don't get a chance to see and experience this sort of thing very often. Anyone can come here, but dad especially loves it when children who are ill, or who don't have much money, visit and have fun with the animals."

Susie paused and looked at her watch. "Come on, you two. There's still a lot to do."

"I wonder how the others are getting on," Nathan said.

It was a fine day, and Luke and Rosie were enjoying their work out in the fields. They worked hard all morning and were ready for a break at twelve o'clock.

"How are you finding all this?" Ben asked them as they walked to the café to meet the others.

"This morning has been great," Rosie answered. "Even though it's been hard work, it's worth it to think we're starting to earn money for the holiday."

"What about the things you're learning about money?" Ben turned to Luke.

Luke stopped to think before he answered. "It's all new to me," he said thoughtfully. "I've never thought much about God before. It does make sense though and I'm willing to try anything to get enough money for the holiday."

They reached the café where Nathan, Bethany and Susie were waiting and were soon tucking in to a big lunch.

"I was ready for this!" Ben said and everyone nodded in agreement.

"We've got a lot done," Rosie exclaimed. "We're more than half way around the fence."

"And we've cleaned out all of the small animal pens," Nathan announced.

"We're going to do the cows and horses this afternoon," Bethany added. "I'm looking forward to that."

"It is hard work though," Luke admitted, rubbing his arms. "My arms and legs are really aching."

Ben smiled. "You've all worked hard this morning. You've been faithful stewards."

"What's a steward, Ben?" asked Rosie.

"A steward is someone who takes care of another person's things," answered Ben. "Another name for a steward is a manager. Today, you are Mr Brent's managers. You are taking care of his nature reserve by working here.

"But all of us are God's stewards. We already learned that He is the owner of everything. In *1 Corinthians 4:2* it says, "*Moreover it is required in stewards, that a man be found faithful (KJV)*." You see, the Lord wants us to be faithful stewards who take good care of His possessions.

"We'll talk more about that back at home tonight," Ben said, as Mr Brent came over.

"You four are good workers," he smiled, ruffling Nathan's hair. "You've done a lot more than I thought you would. Are you ready for that tour?"

"You bet!" Luke jumped up. "I've never been here before, so it will be good to see what I'm a manager of!"

Mr Brent looked puzzled and Ben

laughed. "I'll explain," he said, as they set off for their tour before getting back to work.

*   *   *   *

Later that evening, four tired children joined Ben in the den.

"I'm aching all over," Nathan stretched then sank down onto a box.

"I don't think I'll be able to stay awake for much longer," Bethany yawned.

"We had better get on with the lesson then," Ben chuckled.

"Tell us more about being a steward," Rosie handed Ben his Bible.

"Remember in our last lesson we learned about the part that God plays with money," he replied. "Now we're going to learn about what we are supposed to do with money. You and I are stewards. Who remembers what a steward is?"

"A manager," Luke answered.

"I thought you'd remember that one!" Ben said. "We are managers of God's possessions, and He wants us to be faithful to handle them in a certain way. God wants us to earn money, spend money, save money and give money His way. And where can we find out His ways?"

"In the Bible," said Bethany.

"That's right," said Ben, opening his Bible. "The first thing that's important to understand is found in *Hebrews 4:13*. It says: "*Nothing in all creation is hidden from God's sight. Everything is uncovered and laid bare before the eyes of Him to whom we must give account*." This verse means that the Lord sees everything you do and knows everything you think.

"Did you understand the last part of that verse? It says the Lord looks at everything we do. Someday God will reward those who know Him for all the things they do right, like handling money His way. Let me read *2 Corinthians 5:9-10* to you," Ben said, thumbing through his Bible. "*So we make it our goal to please Him…For we must all appear before the judgement seat of Christ, that each one may receive what is due him for the things done while in the body, whether good or bad*."

"You mean, God knows everything I do and say?" Rosie asked with her eyes wide open.

"Yes, He does, Rosie," Ben answered. "And that would be scary except that He loves us so much. He gave us the Bible as a map to show us how to handle money the right way."

"Well, handling money is easy for me," said Luke.

"I don't have very much."

"Luke," said Ben. "God wants us to be faithful, no matter what we have. It doesn't matter if we have fifty pounds, or only one pound. We are to be faithful with what we have. If you are faithful with a little thing, God knows He can trust you to take care of bigger things. Luke, why don't you read Luke 16:10 for us?" Ben asked, handing him the Bible.

"Ok," said Luke. "*Whoever can be trusted with very little can also be trusted with much*."

"Thanks, Luke," said Ben. "That is a great verse to remind us to do a good job with little things.

"There's one more thing you should know about being a steward," he continued. "You must take care of other people's things before you can expect God to give you things of your own. Let me read *Luke 16:12* to you. "*And if you are not faithful with other people's things, why should you be trusted with things of your own? (NLT)*"

* * * *

"Because you were faithful while working at Pinewoods today, Mr Brent paid you money so you can save for the holiday," said Ben. "And now is a good time to begin learning how to budget your money."

"What's a budget?" asked Nathan.

"A budget is a plan that helps you spend money wisely. It will help you get what is important to you," Ben answered.

"Like going on holiday?" Bethany questioned.

"That's right, Bethany," Ben replied. "Because going on holiday is important to you, you must be careful not to spend your money on other things that are not as important."

"I've made something that will help you begin to budget," he continued as he began picking small boxes up from the corner where they were stacked. "I want each of you to have three of these boxes. One is labelled Giving, another Saving and the last Spending."

"When you receive money, decide how much you want to give and put it in the box labelled Giving. Put the amount you want to save in the Saving box and what you want to spend in the Spending box. This way you can count the money any time in your Saving box to find out how much more you need for the holiday. And you will always know how much you can spend just by looking at the Spending box."

"But what happens when the Spending box is empty and I want to buy something?" asked Luke.

"You'll have to wait until you get money to put in the Spending box," replied Rosie.

"That's right," said Ben, smiling. "You don't want to take it out of the Giving and Saving boxes."

"This is a great idea!" exclaimed Bethany. "I can see why I've never been able to save before. I've always spent all my money. I've never saved to buy the things that are really important."

"Bethany, you've just taken a big step toward going on holiday," said Ben. "Remember, using these boxes to budget will help you to become a faithful steward."

The four children collected their boxes ready to go.

"When can we have our next lesson, Ben?" Nathan asked.

"I've never known you this keen to learn before!" teased Ben.

"But this is great because it's helping us do something we really want to," Nathan explained.

"It will help you all through your life if you remember these lessons," Ben said. "Soon I'll be starting university and I'd get into big trouble if I hadn't learnt to budget, and be sensible with my money. As far as the next lesson goes, I'm free next Saturday afternoon if you want to come round again."

"Great," said Luke. "I'll be busy in the morning. Mum has said she'll give me some money if I clean the car and help her at home. That will be more to go in my Saving box!"

"You're getting the message," smiled Ben. "See you all next week."

Memorise a verse

Moreover it is required in stewards, that a man be found faithful (1 Corinthians 4:2, KJV).

Answer these questions

1. Look up the word *steward* in the dictionary. What does it mean?

_____

_____

_____

2. Read *1 Corinthians 4:2*. According to this verse what are stewards required to do?

_____

_____

_____

3. Look up *Luke 16:10*. Why do you think it is important to be faithful with small things?

_____

4. Read *Luke 16:1-2*. Why did the master remove the unfaithful steward from his job?

_____

_____

_____

5. Read *Hebrews 4:13*. Does the Lord see everything you do? How will knowing this help you change any of the ways you act and spend money?

_____

_____

_____

_____

6. Read *2 Corinthians 5:9-10*. What will happen to us in the future? Why is this important for us to understand?

_____

_____

_____

Work it out

Get or make three small boxes and label one Giving, one Saving and one Spending. Decide how much you want to put in each one when you receive the money.

For the next two weeks, write in the space below how much money you received and how much you put in the Giving, Saving and Spending.

Money I received	Giving	Saving	Spending
_____	_____	_____	_____
_____	_____	_____	_____
_____	_____	_____	_____
_____	_____	_____	_____
_____	_____	_____	_____
_____	_____	_____	_____
_____	_____	_____	_____
_____	_____	_____	_____
_____	_____	_____	_____
_____	_____	_____	_____
_____	_____	_____	_____

Write your prayer here

_____
_____
_____
_____
_____

Studying with a group
Get ready for the next chapter

Read chapter 4, memorise *Proverbs 22:7* and answer the questions on page 31 then complete the *Work It Out* exercise on page 32.

The mobile phone problem

Luke whistled loudly as he polished his mum's car. He felt very pleased with himself. The money was building up in his Saving box and, for the first time since Mr Lewis announced the holiday, Luke could picture himself in the Welsh mountains, having fun with his friends.

"And that's one of the best things," Luke said to himself as he reached for the window cleaner. "Having friends like Nathan, Rosie and Beth to work with. It's much better than doing it on my own."

"Are you talking to yourself?" Luke's eighteen year old sister, Jess came up behind him. Luke grinned and threw a cloth at her. Even Jess could not dampen his mood this morning.

"I'm going out," Jess threw the cloth back. "I've got an offer for you though. Steve is buying me a new mobile phone and I'll sell you my old one if you want."

Luke stopped working and looked at Jess. "I'd love a phone of my own," he said. "But you know I haven't got the money to buy one – even your old one. It's OK for you, having a rich boyfriend!"

"Well, I was thinking," began Jess slowly. "You could give me some money now, then a little each month until it's paid for."

"I could do that!" Luke sounded excited. "What about making calls?"

"I could get you a top-up card to put in your phone each month and you pay me back," Jess offered. "Although, if you can't pay me one month, you'd have to pay extra the next. I don't want to lose money on this."

"That sounds great!" said Luke. "I've wanted a phone for ages."

"We'll sort it tonight when I get home," Jess waved and ran off down the drive. "Enjoy the rest of your cleaning!"

Luke went back to work, but his mind was on Jess' offer. Maybe he could use a little money from the Saving box; he would soon pay it back and this was for something important, just like Ben had said.

Luke was still excited about the mobile phone when Rosie came to call for him after lunch. He couldn't wait to get to Nathan's to tell everyone about it.

"Slow down Luke!" Rosie was out of breath. "What's the big hurry?"

"Wait 'til you hear my news!" Luke called over his shoulder.

They arrived at Nathan's and Luke told the others about Jess' offer.

"Well, that's just great, Luke," Nathan said disgustedly. "We're trying to save to go on holiday, and you're going to spend your money on a mobile phone."

"You haven't heard the best part yet," Luke said. "Jess said I can pay her just a little each month until I get it paid for. And she'll only charge me extra for the top-up card if I can't pay her one month."

"Luke, that might not be such a good idea," warned Rosie. "My parents are always talking about how hard it is to pay what they owe. They say they wish they had never started borrowing."

"I'm only talking about a mobile phone," Luke answered, a touch of hurt in his voice.

*   *   *   *

Bethany headed for the door. "I think we should ask Ben what he thinks," she suggested.

"That's a good idea," agreed Nathan. "It's time to meet him in the den anyway."

Minty followed them down the garden path and into the den. Luke laughed as the dog licked his nose. "You understand what a good chance this is for me, don't you, girl?" he said as he scratched the top of Minty's head. Everyone laughed as the big dog barked in agreement.

"What's this about a good chance?" Ben asked as he walked into the den.

Ben listened carefully as Luke told him about his sister's offer. Luke's eyes shimmered with excitement as he asked, "Isn't it great? I can still use most of my money for the holiday and I won't have to pay all the money for the phone to Jess until later."

When Luke finished, Ben reached for his Bible, turned a few pages, and then kindly said, "Luke, listen to this verse and then tell me what you think it means: *Just as the rich rule the poor, so the borrower is servant to the lender (Proverbs 22:7, NLT).*"

Luke listened to Ben read with a puzzled expression on his face. "I don't know," he answered. "It says something about servants who borrow."

"I know," said Rosie. "It says if you borrow money from someone, you become that person's servant."

"That's exactly what it means," Ben replied. "Until you pay off a debt you owe, a part of the money you earn will have to be paid to the lender. Let's take a look at what the Bible says about debt.

"Nathan, look up *Romans 13:8* and read it to us."

Nathan read aloud. "*Keep out of debt and owe no man anything* (AMP). Ben, this says not to owe anything to anyone," he commented when he finished.

"That's right," Ben agreed. "That's because we become their servants just as we read a minute ago. In the Old Testament, if God's people obeyed Him, God said that one of their rewards would be that they would not be in debt."

He turned to Bethany. "That's what verses 1, 2 and 12 in *Deuteronomy 28* tell us. Bethany, will you read them to us?"

Bethany read, "*If you fully obey the Lord…all these blessings will come upon you…you will lend to many nations, but will borrow from none.*"

"Later in the same chapter the Lord says that when they disobeyed, they borrowed money and got into debt," said Ben.

"But sometimes you have to owe people for some things, don't you? My mum's always talking about the mortgage on our house," Luke protested.

Ben smiled. "You're right, Luke. There might be times when it is all right to borrow money, such as when you buy a house. But there is a big difference between acting wisely by working hard to earn the money you need and acting unwisely by always buying things on credit."

"One of the biggest reasons people borrow money is that they aren't satisfied with what they have. They want something better right away. What are some of the things that each of you would like to have right now?"

"The money to go on the school holiday," Nathan said.

"I'd like a new flute now," said Bethany. "My music teacher said I could play a lot better if I had a new one."

"I'd like a new pair of trainers," added Rosie. "My old ones are black and I want some purple ones."

"And I'd like a brand new mobile phone of my own," said Luke. "Then I wouldn't have to buy Jess' old one."

"Those are good examples," said Ben. "Each of you wants something right away because you aren't satisfied with things the way they are. Can you see how easy it is when you are dissatisfied to make unwise decisions that can get you into debt? Yet, in most cases, if we just learn to wait, we can find ways to earn the money for what we want – just like you're doing for the holiday."

"There's a great story found in *2 Kings 4:1-7* about a widow with two sons who found a way to get out of debt with just a small jar of oil."

"A jar of oil?" Bethany questioned. "Tell us about her."

"Long ago in Israel there was a young mother who was married to a prophet. They had two young sons. They borrowed some money, and sadly one day the father died before he could pay it back."

"In those days, if you could not repay a debt, you were sold as a slave. Soon after the father's death, the man who had loaned the money to them demanded that it be paid back. But the poor widow had no money, and her two boys were going to become slaves."

"The boys' mother was very upset. She had no way to earn enough money to pay the debt. But she knew a prophet named Elisha, and she went to ask him what she should do."

"Elisha was touched by the woman's story, so he asked, 'what do you have?'"

'I have nothing,' the mother answered, 'except a small jar of oil.'

"Elisha told her to collect as many empty jars and pots as she could from her neighbours. Then he instructed her, 'take them to your house and pour the oil from your little jar into each empty pot and jar.'"

"The woman hurried home and told her boys to help her gather all the containers they could find. When they had them in their house, they filled the jars just as Elisha had told her. The boys had never seen so much oil. The oil didn't stop flowing until all the jars were full!"

"Elisha told her to sell the oil. Then he said, 'When you have the money, pay the man what you owe him. There will be enough money left for you to take care of your family.'"

"The mother was very thankful, and the boys learned an important lesson about borrowing money. But they also learned that God loved them and would take care of them, as He did by multiplying the oil."

*   *   *   *

As Ben finished his story, he said, "God loves us and will take care of us. But we need to learn that borrowing money can sometimes lead to trouble."

"Today, when someone borrows money that person has to pay interest on the money borrowed. Does anyone know what interest is?" Ben asked.

Rosie said, "I've heard my parents say that they have to pay a lot of interest on their debts, but I'm not sure what it is."

Ben explained, "When people borrow money, they have to pay back more than they actually borrowed. This extra money they have to pay is called interest. And interest can be very expensive. If you borrow a hundred pounds, you may have to pay as much as twenty pounds a year in interest until you pay it back."

Everyone gasped. "That's a lot of extra money!" Nathan exclaimed.

"Luke, think about the top-up cards your sister offered to buy," Ben continued. "You could end up paying much more money than the cards cost in the first place. You will worry about those debts all the time, wondering if you will ever get them paid. In that way, you will be a servant to your sister until you pay her back."

As Ben talked, Luke looked very uncomfortable. "I don't think I want to do that," he said. "I'm going to tell Jess that I don't want to buy her mobile phone now. Instead I'm going to wait until I have enough money to pay cash for it."

"That's a very good decision, Luke," Ben said nodding.

The friends sat quietly for a few minutes, thinking about what Ben had said. Suddenly Bethany jumped up.

"I nearly forgot with all this excitement about the mobile phone!" she exclaimed, pulling an envelope out of her pocket. "Dad gave me another clue to God's secret of handling money this morning."

"What does it say?" Nathan asked, as the other three gathered around Bethany.

She pulled a piece of paper out of the envelope. "It is something you do, not something you have," she read.

Ben smiled. "Keep thinking about it," he encouraged them. "I know you'll discover the secret."

"We can hardly wait," Rosie said.

They had no idea that a surprise would be waiting for them in the den the following week.

Memorise a verse

Just as the rich rule the poor, so the borrower is servant to the lender (Proverbs 22:7, NLT).

Answer these questions

1. How does the dictionary describe *debt*?

_____

_____

2. Why do you think most people go into debt?

_____

_____

_____

_____

_____

3. Read *Romans 13:8*. What does this verse say about owing money?

_____

_____

_____

_____

4. Read *Proverbs* 22:7. What does this verse say about someone who borrows money?

_____

_____

_____

_____

_____

5. Why do you think the Lord wants us to stay out of debt?

_____

_____

_____

_____

_____

Work it out

List any money you owe and who loaned you the money.
Then describe how you plan to pay it back.

Money I owe	Who loaned me the money	How I plan to pay it back
_____	_____	_____
_____	_____	_____
_____	_____	_____
_____	_____	_____
_____	_____	_____

Write your prayer here

_____

_____

_____

_____

_____

_____

_____

→ Studying with a group
Get ready for the next chapter

Read chapter 5, memorise *Proverbs 12:15* and answer the questions on page 39 then complete the *Work It Out* exercise on page 40.

The puppies arrive

Bethany sat at the kitchen table, eating toast. It was early but she was keen to get ready for the day ahead. The four friends were going to work at Pinewoods again and were thrilled that the money in their Savings boxes was starting to build up.

"I never thought it would be this much fun to earn money," Bethany said to herself. "I'm so glad mum and dad made me do this."

"That's good to hear, Bethany," said her dad as he came into the kitchen.

Bethany jumped up. "Dad, I thought you were still in bed. You scared me!"

Mr Kasanga laughed. "What are your plans for today?" he asked.

Bethany was about to answer when the telephone rang loudly.

"Who could that be, so early on a Saturday morning?" wondered Mr Kasanga as Bethany answered the phone.

"Beth!" It was Nathan, sounding very excited. "Can you come over? Minty is about to have her puppies. Get here as quickly as you can!"

Bethany nearly dropped the phone in her excitement. "Dad, can you take me to Nathan's right away? Minty is going to have her puppies."

Mr Kasanga nodded. "Get your things," he said. "We'll pick up Luke and Rosie on the way. I'm sure they won't want to miss this either."

Fifteen minutes later the four friends gathered in Nathan's garden.

"This is so exciting!" said Rosie. "I never thought we'd be here when Minty had the puppies."

"Can we watch?" asked Luke.

"You can do more than that," Susie appeared out of the den. "I'm going to need your help. But you must do exactly what I tell you. You won't be able to help unless you promise to follow my advice."

"We'll do exactly what you say," promised Nathan.

"Of course we will," agreed Bethany. "Where is Minty? Why did Mrs Howard send us out here?"

"Ben made a special box for Minty to have her puppies in," explained Susie. "It's the safest place for her and the puppies when they are born. We tried to put it in the house but Minty kept coming out here to the den. I guess she wants to have her puppies here."

"That's wonderful!" exclaimed Rosie.

"But shouldn't she and the puppies be somewhere warm?" asked Luke.

Susie nodded. "You're right, Luke. If it was winter, Minty definitely couldn't have her puppies in the den. But this time of year it won't be a problem."

"Tell us what to do, Susie," said Bethany eagerly.

Susie began giving them instructions. "Nathan, run and ask your mum for some towels and a pair of scissors. We may not need them but it's good to be prepared just in case. Rosie, go with him and find the vet's number in the phone book. I'd like to have it handy just in case. Luke and Bethany come with me but keep quiet and don't crowd Minty."

Luke and Bethany followed Susie into the den. Ben was already there, stroking Minty's head as she lay on the floor. He stood up and beckoned Bethany.

"Come over here and stroke Minty's head for a few minutes," he whispered. "It'll help to keep her calm."

"Luke, your job is to make sure Minty doesn't try to get out of the box," Susie instructed. "She may try to hide herself away when the pain gets bad but that would be dangerous for her and the puppies. She needs to stay here where we can help her."

"How do you know what to do?" asked Rosie, as she came in quietly, followed by Nathan with the towels and scissors.

"God created Minty to know what to do," Susie

replied. "All we need to do is help her a little bit." She motioned to Nathan and Rosie. "Stay here by the door, you two. We don't want to make Minty nervous."

The children watched quietly, but with growing excitement as Minty became restless. Susie beckoned to Bethany to move by the others. "It's time, isn't it, girl?" she said to Minty in a soothing voice.

The children gasped in excitement as the first puppy was born. Minty examined the newborn puppy and licked it all over. Then she lay back down with the puppy nestled closely to her.

"Is that it?" whispered Luke.

"No," Susie shook her head. "I know there's more than one puppy. Minty will rest for a few minutes now before the next puppy is born."

"Look," said Nathan. "She's keeping the puppy warm."

"She's doing really well," agreed Ben. "Isn't it amazing that she's never had puppies before, yet she knows exactly what to do?"

The children did not have to wait long before the second puppy was born, closely followed by a third. Minty licked each one and made sure they were nestled against her, just as she had with the first. Finally, a fourth puppy made an appearance.

"This looks like the last one," said Susie. "It's the smallest, the runt of the litter."

Minty licked the puppy, but unlike the other three, the smallest puppy wriggled away from her and made its way unsteadily to the other side of the box. Bethany began to move forward but Susie put a hand on her arm.

"Let's see what happens first," she said. "We need to let Minty sort this so she can bond with her puppy. Hopefully, the puppy will cry and Minty will fetch it. If not, she may abandon it."

"Oh, I hope not," Rosie gasped, and the four children waited with their breath held. After what seemed like forever, the small puppy whimpered. Minty lifted her head then slowly walked over to it. She gently picked up the puppy in her mouth, carrying it back to join the others.

The four friends let out a sigh of relief.

"Thank goodness for that!" Nathan voiced what they were all thinking.

"I was beginning to worry," Susie admitted.

"What would have happened if Minty had abandoned the puppy?" asked Luke.

"We would have had to look after it," explained Susie. "But the puppy is much better off with its mother."

"When can we hold the puppies?" Bethany asked eagerly.

"Not for six weeks or so," said Susie. "They need time to get to know their mum first. Look, they're drinking milk from her now."

The children watched for a few more minutes as the four puppies settled down to drink. Minty started to lick them again one by one.

"She looks very pleased with herself!" said Rosie.

"Come on, guys," Ben stood up and stretched. "Let's leave Minty and her puppies in peace. Looks like we'll have to do our lesson in the house today."

They all settled down in the lounge.

"Thanks for your help," Susie said. "You listened to my advice and did just what I told you to do. You were great helpers." She stood up and reached for her keys. "I need to get home now, but I'll see you all at Pinewoods later."

After they had said goodbye to Susie, Ben said, "The way you listened to advice today would have made a king in the Bible very happy. His name was

Solomon. He was the wisest man who ever lived, and he wrote most of the book of *Proverbs*. In today's lesson I want you to learn what Solomon said about seeking wise advice."

"Solomon told us that a wise person seeks counsel. Counsel is another word for advice. *Proverbs 12:15* says: *The way of a fool is right in his own eyes, but a wise man is he who listens to counsel (NASB)*."

Ben picked up his Bible. "Listen to these two verses from *Proverbs* and see if you can tell me why it is good to listen to counsel.

Pride only breeds quarrels, but wisdom is found in those who take advice. (Proverbs 13:10)."

"I know the answer to that one," said Rosie. "Listening to advice can help us to stay out of arguments and quarrels."

"That's right," said Ben. "Many people have money problems because they do not seek counsel. Now, how about this verse?

"Plans fail for lack of counsel, but with many advisors they succeed. (Proverbs 15:22)."

"I know," Nathan said. "Listening to advice will help us to be successful when we are making plans."

"Like earning the money for our holiday," added Luke. "Your advice is really helping us with that, Ben."

Ben nodded. "Good advice gives you suggestions and ideas that will help you to make the right decisions. There are several places for you to go to get good advice."

"The best advice is found in the Bible. Did you know that the Bible contains the very words of God. Bethany, please look up 2 *Timothy 3:16* and read it to us."

"Ok," Bethany said, reaching for the Bible. *"All Scripture is inspired by God and is useful to teach us what is true and to make us realize what is wrong in our lives. It corrects us when we are wrong and teaches us to do what is right (NLT)."*

"That's why it's so important for you to read the Bible every single day," said Ben. "It will keep you close to God and give you answers to your problems.

"And the Bible also tells us to ask godly people for their advice. Listen to *Psalm 37:30-31: The godly offer good counsel; they teach right from wrong. They have made God's law their own, so they will never slip from his path. (NLT)."*

"My dad always has good advice for me," said Nathan.

"You're right," agreed Ben. "Our parents are a great source of counsel. Let me read what King Solomon said in *Proverbs 6:20-22: My son, keep your father's commands and do not forsake your mother's teaching. Bind them upon your heart for ever; fasten them around your neck. When you walk, they will guide you; when you sleep, they will watch over you; when you awake, they will speak to you."*

"Asking your parents' advice is a good way to honour them and will help build a close relationship with them. But we can also ask God for His counsel when we pray. One of God's names is Wonderful Counsellor. Listen to what *Psalm 32:8* has to say about the Lord's counsel," *I (the Lord) will instruct you and teach you in the way which you should go; I will counsel you and watch over you."*

"Ben, what about fortune-tellers?" asked Luke. "My aunt went to see one a while ago when she didn't know what to do."

"That's a good question," answered Ben. "The Bible tells us never to seek the advice of fortune-tellers, psychics or mediums. *Do not turn to mediums or spiritists; do not seek them out…I am the Lord your God (Leviticus 19:31)*."

"That also means we should never read horoscopes or play with Ouija boards too, doesn't it?" asked Bethany.

"Never," agreed Ben. "Always stay away from them.

"We also need to avoid the advice of wicked people," Ben continued. "In fact, *Psalm 1:1* tells us that we will be blessed if we do not seek advice from a wicked person.

Ben stood up and pulled a piece of paper from his pocket. "I've got another clue to help you discover God's secrets to handling money. Bethany's dad gave it me this morning and it fits in really well with what we've been learning today. Are you trying to work out the secret?"

"It's really tough," said Rosie. "So far we know that when we discover it, it will mean more to us than going on the holiday."

"And it's not something we have but something we do," added Nathan.

"Let me read the next clue," said Ben. "You will find the answer in God's Word."

Ben looked at the four friends but they still appeared puzzled. "Don't worry," he smiled. "Pretty soon the clues will lead you to the discovery." He stood up and stretched. "Now, don't forget what you've learnt so far. I'm working away for the next month so we'll carry on with the lessons when I get back. But don't stop earning money for your Saving boxes!"

"Ben," Nathan said. "What do you think we should name the puppies?"

"Well," Ben said. "There are four puppies and four of you. I'll ask Susie to let us know whether they are male or female, then each of you can think up a name for one of them. And when we get together next time, you can tell me."

"That's a great idea!" Bethany said excitedly. "I can't wait to see them again."

Little did they know the trouble they were soon to experience.

Memorise a verse

The way of a fool is right in his own eyes, but a wise man is he who listens to counsel (Proverbs 12:15, NASB).

Answer these questions

1. What does it mean to seek counsel or advice?

_____

_____

_____

2. Are there reasons why you think you do not ask for advice? If there are, please list them?

_____

_____

_____

3. What are some of the good things you have learned from seeking counsel?

_____

_____

_____

4. Read *Psalm 16:7* and *Psalm 32:8*. What are some of the ways the Lord counsels us?

_____

_____

_____

5. Read *Psalm 119:105, 2 Timothy 3:16-17,* and *Hebrews 4:12*. Each verse tells us something about the Scriptures. Write what each verse says in the space below.

Psalm 119:105

_____

_____

2 Timothy 3:16-17

_____

_____

Hebrews 4:12

_____

_____

6. Why do you think you should avoid the counsel of wicked people?

_____

_____

_____

Work it out

Make a list of the people who will make good counsellors for you, and don't forget to put down parents/carers. Write down a question to ask each of them about money. Then ask them!

Good Counsellor	Question to ask about money

Write your prayer here

_____

_____

_____

_____

Studying with a group
Get ready for the next chapter

Read chapter 6, memorise _Leviticus 19:11_ and answer the questions on page 47 then complete the _Work It Out_ exercise on page 48.

Lost and found

"What did you think about that storm last night?" Nathan asked as the four friends walked home from school together on a Wednesday afternoon six weeks after the puppies had been born.

"I've never seen so much lightening," said Rosie. "I couldn't get to sleep for hours."

"And what about the thunder?" added Luke. "It was so loud."

"Were Minty and the puppies alright?" Bethany asked.

Nathan nodded. "Ben and I stayed with them to begin with. We tried to bring them in the house but they still like it out in the den, especially at night. Mum was going to check on them today."

"I'm glad we've got another lesson now," said Rosie. "It seems ages since the last one with Ben being away. And I can't wait to see the puppies again."

"We've got to name them today," Nathan reminded the others. "Susie says there are two boy puppies and two girls – just right for us!"

"Perfect!" Bethany exclaimed as they walked through the gate at Nathan's. "I was hoping mine would be a girl. I've got an idea for her name already."

The children ran down the garden path and pushed open the door of the den, which had not been locked since Minty and her puppies had lived there.

"Look at them!" said Rosie. "They've grown already!"

Bethany threw down her school bag and knelt by Minty, closely followed by Rosie.

"They're gorgeous!" she exclaimed. "Can I hold one?"

Nathan nodded and reached for one of the puppies. "I already have. Here's my favourite - the biggest one. I'm going to call him Goliath."

"He's not that big!" Rosie giggled.

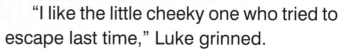

"I like the little cheeky one who tried to escape last time," Luke grinned.

"He's the other boy puppy," Nathan told them.

Luke looked around the den. "Hey, Nathan," he said. "Where is he? I can only see three puppies."

Nathan looked up from stroking Goliath. Bethany was holding a puppy and another was snuggled up against Minty.

"I don't know," he said, putting Goliath down. "He must be here somewhere."

The children looked all over the den but could not find the smallest puppy anywhere. Bethany looked worried.

"The puppy is so young and small, Nathan," she said. "He couldn't have got far on his own."

"And there was that awful storm last night," Rosie added. "This isn't good."

"Let's find mum," said Nathan. "She might know."

They had not gone far down the path when they met Mrs Howard and Ben, both looking upset.

"Mum, the smallest puppy is missing!" Nathan cried.

"I know," Mrs Howard nodded sadly. "When I came to check them this morning, he was gone. Ben and I have searched the garden and the house but can't find him anywhere."

Bethany was close to tears. "What could have happened to him?" she asked shakily.

"One of three things," Ben replied. "A fox could have killed him; he could have wandered off by himself; or someone could have stolen him."

"Stolen him!" Luke said with a touch of anger in his voice. "Who could have been so mean to do that?"

"I read in the paper just this morning that some pets have been stolen in the area over the last few weeks," said Mrs Howard. "If I had known that earlier, I never would have let Minty and the puppies stay in the den. I'm so sorry."

"It's not your fault, mum," said Nathan, giving her a hug. "Come to think of it, I did hear Minty barking a lot during the storm last night. She could have been barking at a thief. I should have checked up on her."

"What can we do?" Rosie asked in a worried voice.

"I think we should pray," suggested Bethany as they walked slowly back to the den.

"Good idea," answered Ben. "Remember what we learnt in the second lesson – God is in control of everything. He knows exactly what happened to the puppy and where he is. We'll ask God to protect him and to give us His wisdom on what we should do."

Everyone sat down on the upturned boxes that were their seats in the den. Minty lay by Luke, so close that she was nearly on top of his feet.

"Poor Minty," Luke stroked her. "Are you missing your puppy?"

They bowed their heads while Ben prayed. After he finished he said, "I know we're not feeling great but let's do the next lesson about God's ways of handling money. We might be able to do more to find the puppy when my dad gets home."

He stopped for a second then continued. "You know, maybe someone stole the puppy because he didn't know that God wants us to always be honest. Nathan, do you remember that time the shop assistant gave you too much change when you paid for your magazine, and you were going to keep it? After we talked about it, what did you do?"

"I returned the extra money to her," Nathan answered. "And I remember you told me about the verse in *Proverbs* that says God hates dishonesty."

"That's right," said Ben with a smile. "*Proverbs 20:23* says, *The Lord detests double standards; he is not pleased by dishonest scales (NLT). Leviticus 19:11* says, *you shall not steal, nor deal falsely, nor lie to one another (NASB).*"

"He wants us to be completely honest in every way, even with small things. Abraham in *Genesis 14:22-23* is a wonderful example of a person who decided to be honest in small things. Listen to what he said, *'I have raised my hand to the Lord, God Most High, Creator of heaven and earth, and have taken an oath that I will accept nothing belonging to you, not even a thread or the thong of a sandal.'* Abraham promised God he wasn't even going to take something as small as a thread from someone else."

"Guys, have any of you ever been dishonest?" Ben asked.

They were quiet. Finally Rosie said, "I took some sweets from a shop. I didn't feel good about it, but I didn't understand God wanted me to be so honest."

Then Luke said, "I stole a CD from one of Jess' friends."

Bethany blushed and said, "I haven't been honest during some of my maths tests. I struggle with maths at school."

Ben smiled. "I'm so proud that you were brave enough to tell me those things. Let's look more closely at what God says about honesty, and maybe you will want to make a promise like Abraham."

He opened his Bible to *Romans 13:9-10* and read, "*For the commandments say…you must not steal. You must not covet. These commandments are summed up in this one commandment: 'Love your neighbour as yourself.' Love does no wrong to others, so love fulfils the requirements of God's law.*" (NLT)." Ben continued, "Any time we're dishonest, we hurt another person – just the way we are hurting now because someone may have stolen the puppy."

"Let's look at Daniel, one of my favourite people in the Bible. His life can also help us understand why it's important to be honest."

"As a young boy, Daniel was taken captive to live in Babylon after his country was defeated in war. But even though he was in a strange new land, Daniel decided to always be honest. The king recognised his honesty, so he asked Daniel to serve in his palace."

"When Daniel had become an old man, a new king named Darius decided to make Daniel the chief ruler of his kingdom. This made some evil people very jealous. They watched him carefully to see if he was doing anything dishonestly so they could tell the king. But Daniel was always honest."

"Finally, these evil men thought of a plan to kill Daniel. They went to the king and asked him to make a law that no one could pray to anyone except King Darius for thirty days. If anyone broke this law, they were to be thrown into a den of lions."

"Even though Daniel knew about the law, he still knelt and prayed to God three times every day. When the evil men discovered that Daniel had broken the law, they told the king."

"At last Darius understood why the evil men had suggested such a law. Even though he liked Daniel, he had no choice but to throw him into the lion's den. Then, with a heavy heart he returned to his palace, unable to sleep all night."

"With the first light of dawn, the king hurried to the den, and cried out, *'Daniel, servant of the living God, has your God, whom you serve continually, been able to rescue you from the lions?'*

"Daniel answered, *'O king, live forever! My God sent His angel, and he shut the mouths of the lions…because I was found innocent'* (Daniel 6:20-22). You see, when we are honest, it pleases God."

"What should we do if we've already been dishonest?" Rosie asked sheepishly.

"God teaches us to return anything we have taken that doesn't belong to us," Ben said. "In fact, the Bible tells us that if we get anything dishonestly, we must return it to its owner with something extra – this is called restitution. Restitution is a way to say, 'I am sorry. Please forgive me.' In the New Testament, Zaccheus gave us a good example of restitution. Nathan, read what he said in *Luke 19:8.*"

"*If I have cheated anybody out of anything, I will pay back four times the amount*," read Nathan.

"Honesty and restitution are hard because so many people around us are dishonest," said Ben.

Suddenly Luke jumped up, shouting, "did you hear that noise?"

Minty also bounded up and started to bark. Luke picked up the box he was sitting on and everyone gasped as they saw a lost, sleepy puppy stretching with a big yawn and a whimper.

"He's here!" Luke shouted. "The puppy's been here all the time!"

Minty lay down next to the puppy and immediately started to lick him all over.

"She's saying 'welcome back!'" Bethany said happily, as they all watched in relief.

"Do you know, I think Minty knew the puppy was there all along," said Nathan. "Did you see how close she lay to Luke's box the whole time?"

"But how did he get under there?" Rosie wondered.

"I don't suppose we'll ever know," said Ben with a smile. "He must have been very scared in the storm. He certainly found a good hiding place. He had us all fooled!"

Luke stroked the little puppy with a smile.

"I'd like to call this one Cheeky," he said.

The others laughed. "That name suits him very well!" Ben said.

Bethany picked up one of the other puppies. "This was the first girl puppy to be born," she commented. "I'll call her Eve, because that was the name of the first woman God created."

"And the name of my puppy will be Hope," said Rosie, "because I hope we can go on holiday."

"Those are great names," said Ben smiling. "How much money have you saved towards the holiday?"

"We have almost half the money we need," replied Nathan. "But we only have six weeks left. When are we going to do the garden so we can earn some more money?"

"Next week," said Ben. "This Saturday, Mr Brent has asked for your help with something else. He is doing a free clinic at Pinewoods for people who can't afford to go to the vet for advice or small problems with their pets. A lot of people are expected to come, and he'll need all of our help to keep things running smoothly. But the clinic can't afford to pay anyone, so you'll have to volunteer your time."

"That's all right," said Rosie and the others nodded. "It'll be good to help people care for their pets."

"Thanks for your willingness to give your time," Ben said. "Let's meet here early for breakfast on Saturday, and then we'll have the next lesson before we go to Pinewoods. We'll learn what God says about giving."

"Now, come on," Ben stood up. "Let's go and tell my mum we've found the puppy – and given him a new name!"

Memorise a verse

You shall not steal, nor deal falsely, nor lie to one another (Leviticus 19:11, NASB).

Answer these questions

1. Read *Leviticus 19:11* and *Exodus 20:15*. According to these verses, what does the Lord say about being honest in small things?

_____

_____

2. Look up *Luke 16:10*. Why do you think Jesus said we should be honest in small things?

_____

_____

_____

3. Are you honest – even in small things?

_____

_____

_____

4. If you are not always honest, what will you do to change?

_____

_____

_____

5. Look up the word *restitution* in the dictionary. What does this mean to you?

_____

_____

_____

6. What should you do if you have taken something dishonestly?

_____

_____

_____

7. What was the most important thing you learned from reading this chapter?

_____

_____

Work it out

Let God show you when and how you were dishonest and plan below to put it right.

How I was dishonest	Who did it affect	How I plan to put it right

Write your prayer here

Studying with a group
Get ready for the next chapter

Read chapter 7, memorise *Acts 20:35* and answer the questions on pages 55 and 56, then complete the *Work It Out* exercise.

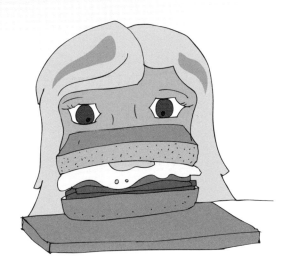

A kitten called Tommy

It was Saturday morning and the four children sat around the table at Nathan's house chattering excitedly. The smell of eggs and bacon wafted around the room.

"This smell is making me hungry!" Luke commented. "If it tastes as good as it smells I can't wait to get started!"

"Not long now," Mr Howard called. "Two of you come over here and help me make these sandwiches."

"My dad makes the best egg and bacon sandwiches ever!" said Nathan as he got up to help.

Ben walked in through the door.

"Looks like I'm just in time," he grinned as Rosie handed him a plate. "Let's thank God for the food then we can all start eating."

Ben prayed then there was quiet for the first time that morning as they all enjoyed their breakfast. When they had finished, Ben pushed his plate away and stretched.

"Are you ready for the clinic this morning?" he asked.

"You bet," Luke spoke for them all.

"There will be a lot of people there," Ben explained. "Your job will be to make sure there is a record of every pet that gets seen."

"We can do that," agreed Bethany and the others nodded.

"You are giving your time to help others and Mr Brent is really grateful," Ben said. "And you know, I also appreciate your great attitude.

"Having the right attitude when we give money is important too," he continued. "Nathan, look up *1 Corinthians 13:3*. Read it and tell us what you think it says about our attitude."

Nathan read, "*If I give all my possessions to feed the poor...but do not have love, it profits me nothing.* I've never thought about this before," he said with a puzzled expression on his face. "It says even if I gave everything away, but did it without love; it wouldn't do me any good."

"You're right," said Ben nodding. "Bethany, will you please read *2 Corinthians 9:7*?"

"Of course," said Bethany. *"God loves a cheerful giver."*

"But how can we always give with love and be cheerful?" asked Rosie. "Sometimes I just don't want to give, especially when I'm working hard to save money for something I really want – like going on the school holiday."

* * * *

"That's a good question," Ben answered. "If you four don't remember anything else about giving, remember this. You should give every gift just as if you are giving to Jesus – even though it is going to be used to help others. And we can be loving and cheerful when we do that. Giving to God is one way to thank Him for making us, loving us, providing food for us, and for dying on a cross so that our sins could be forgiven."

"I'd never thought about that," Bethany spoke up. "Ben, there's a verse in the Bible that says something about giving instead of receiving, isn't there?"

"You're thinking of *Acts 20:35*," said Ben. "It says, *remember the words of the Lord Jesus, that He Himself said, 'It is more blessed to give than to receive'.*"

"What!" exclaimed Luke in disbelief. "Are you sure about that? How can it be better to give than to receive? That doesn't sound right to me."

"I understand, Luke," said Ben smiling. "I didn't believe it either the first time I heard this truth, because we all know how good it feels to receive a gift. But when you start giving, you'll find out that it really is a bigger blessing to give than to receive."

"Just how much of our money does God want us to give away?" asked Rosie with a worried look on her face.

"Well, Rosie, why don't you read *Malachi 3:8-9* for us," Ben responded.

"Ok," Rosie said reaching for the Bible. *"Will a man rob God? Yet you rob Me! But you ask, 'How do we rob you?' In tithes and offerings. You are under a curse – because you are robbing Me."*

"That's hard to understand," Rosie said. "It says something about tithes and robbing God. What's a tithe?"

"A tithe is ten percent of the money you receive," Ben answered. "If you earn a pound, a tithe would be ten pence. In the Old Testament God commanded His people to give a tithe. If they didn't, it was the same thing as robbing Him."

"So if we tithe, that's all we have to give?" asked Nathan.

Ben smiled. "I think the best way to answer you is to tell you a Bible story about a woman who gave everything that she had. One day, Jesus and His disciples were visiting the temple in Jerusalem. Jesus watched a poor widow wearing tattered clothing come into the temple. Although she was poor, her face was radiant because she was so joyful."

"As she passed the box where people gave their money, she took two small copper coins that were worth less than a penny and dropped them into the box."

*   *   *   *

"Listen to what Jesus told His disciples. *'This poor widow has put more into the treasury than all the others. They all gave out of their wealth; but she, out of her poverty'* (Mark 12:43-44)."

Bethany interrupted Ben's story with a question.

"But Ben," she asked "how could she buy food?"

"Remember what we learned in the lesson about God's part?" answered Ben. "He is the One who provides for our needs. The poor widow was trusting God to give her what she needed to live on."

Ben stopped and looked at his watch.

"It's time for us to go to Pinewoods," he said, standing up. "Mr Brent and Susie will have queues of people to look after on their own if we don't get a move on."

"Oh, I nearly forgot!" Rosie exclaimed as they fetched their coats. "My mum said you can all come back to my house for lunch. Is that OK with everyone?"

"Thanks, Rosie," Bethany said and the boys nodded. "That will be great."

When they arrived at Pinewoods, the car park was already filling up with people and animals. There were dogs, cats, rabbits, mice, and Luke even spotted a pet snake, much to his delight!

Susie came out to meet them.

"Nathan and Luke, help the people make a line to this door," she instructed, pointing to a door at the side. "Give each person one of these cards to fill in with their name and address, and try to find out a bit about their pet and what they have come for. Then we'll be quicker when they get inside. You can help them, Ben."

She turned to Rosie and Bethany. "You two, come inside with me. I want you to get a clipboard each and write down briefly what each person asks for, and how my dad helps them. Can you do that?"

The girls nodded and Susie smiled. "Thanks for coming all of you. It's going to make our job a lot easier this morning."

They worked hard and by the time the last person left, they were all ready for a break. They were just getting ready to leave when a battered blue van pulled up. An older lady climbed out and called, "Susie! Fetch your dad. I need him to come over here and give me a hand."

*　　*　　*　　*

"Who's that?" Nathan asked.

"That's Mrs Nicholas," Ben explained. "She loves animals and is often turning up here with all the strays she finds. Come on, let's see what she wants."

They walked over to the van, reaching it at the same time as Susie and Mr Brent. In the back of the van lay a small black kitten whose leg was badly hurt. As Mr Brent started examining the kitten, Mrs Nicholas explained.

"I found him by the side of the road out in the country," she said. "I stopped at the nearby houses but no one knew anything about him. I think someone must have just left him there because they didn't want him. I fed him with a baby bottle, but I can't afford to keep him."

52

"Oh, he's so cute!" said Rosie, reaching over to gently stroke the kitten's back.

Mr Brent checked the kitten's leg carefully and said, "His leg is broken and he will need a splint on it so it can heal."

"Can I hold him?" Rosie asked.

"Sure," Mr Brent said as he laid the kitten carefully in Rosie's arms. "I'll put the splint on his broken leg and then decide what to do with him."

Slowly Rosie carried the little kitten inside. Mr Brent skilfully fitted a splint on his leg.

"I've got an idea," Rosie suddenly said. "Could the kitten stay here at Pinewoods until he's better? I'll do some extra work to earn enough money to pay for his food."

Mr Brent smiled. "That sounds fine to me," he said.

"Then I'll ask mum and dad if I can keep him as my pet," Rosie continued excitedly. "I'm sure they won't mind if I agree to pay for his food."

"Rosie, that's a great idea," said Ben. "I think you're beginning to understand what Jesus meant when He said it is more blessed to give than to receive."

*   *   *   *

Two hours later, the four friends were sitting in Rosie's back garden, watching her younger brother and sister playing. Rosie was still excited about the kitten.

"It's great that your mum agreed to let you keep him," said Nathan.

"I know!" Rosie beamed. "I've never had a pet of my own before. It will be so much fun. I'm going to call him Tommy, I think the name really suits him."

"What's that about giving?" asked a voice as Mr Kasanga joined them in the garden.

"We've had a great day, dad," Bethany told him as she gave him a hug. "Ben taught us that it's better to give than to receive, and I think we've all discovered that today."

"That's a great lesson to learn," smiled Mr Kasanga. "So can any of you guess who God wants us to give to?"

"It's important to give to your church," Nathan answered.

"And to those who are poor," added Luke.

"You're right," said Mr Kasanga. "You're never more like Jesus than when you're giving."

He paused and pulled a small Bible from his back pocket. "Let me read *Matthew 25:37-40 (NASB), Then the righteous will answer Him saying, 'Lord, when did we see You hungry, and feed You, or thirsty, and give You drink?'...The King will answer and say to them, 'Truly I say to you, to the extent that you did it to one of these brothers of Mine, even the least of them, you did it to Me.'*

"God approves of you working to earn and save money for the holiday. But you should also give some of what you earn to others who need it."

"Maybe we could pray that God will show us someone who needs something that we could give," Bethany suggested.

"And maybe that person could help you discover God's secret to handling money," said Mr Kasanga.

"That's another clue, isn't it?" said Luke. "I like that idea. Let's pray right now!"

Mr Kasanga and the four children bowed their heads. One by one, each prayed for God to show them someone who needed something that they could give. It was a prayer that God was going to answer in a very unexpected way.

Memorise a verse

Remember the words of the Lord Jesus, that He Himself said, 'It is more blessed to give than to receive' (Acts 20:35, NASB).

Answer these questions

1. The Lord says it is important to give with the right attitude. Look up *1 Corinthians 13:3* and *2 Corinthians 9:7*. According to these verses, what attitudes should we have when we give?

1 Corinthians 13:3

_____

_____

2 Corinthians 9:7

_____

_____

2. How do you think you can learn to give cheerfully and from a heart filled with love?

_____

_____

3. Do you think it is better to give than to receive a gift? Why?

_____

_____

Look up *Acts 20:35*. How do you think the Lord would answer this question?

_____

_____

4. List the benefits of the giver in *Proverbs 11:24-25* and *Matthew 6:20*.

Proverbs 11:24-25

_____

_____

Matthew 6:20

_____

_____

5. Look up the word *tithe* in the dictionary. What does it mean to tithe?

_____

_____

6. How much of your income do you give?

_____

7. Do you think it is important to give to your church? Why?

_____

_____

8. List the benefits of the giver found in *Proverbs 28:27* and *Matthew 25:34-45*. What do these passages say about giving to the poor?

Proverbs 28:27

_____

_____

Matthew 25:34-45

_____

_____

Work it out

Begin to pray for the Lord to bring someone into your life whom you can help by giving. Then make a list of those whom you want to give to and write down how much you would like to give….Don't forget you should give to the Lord through your church first.

Who I want to give to	How much I want to give
_____	_____
_____	_____
_____	_____

Write your prayer here

_____

_____

_____

_____

Studying with a group
Get ready for the next chapter

Read chapter 8, memorise *Colossians 3:23-24* and answer the questions on pages 63 and 64, then complete the *Work It Out* exercise.

Sleeping in the den

Nathan was getting ready for school on Friday morning when Ben poked his head in through the bedroom door.

"Remind Bethany, Luke and Rosie that we're working on the garden tomorrow," he said. "Tell them to come early as we'll have to work all day to get it cleared."

"Ok," said Nathan, then his eyes lit up with an idea. "Hey Ben, do you think we could have a sleepover in the den tonight? That way, we'll be ready to start first thing in the morning."

"That's not a bad idea," agreed Ben. "You'll have to check with dad and mum though. And do you think you'll get much sleep with you four together?"

"Maybe not!" Nathan grinned. "But it will be fun."

"I'll pitch my tent on the lawn and sleep out as well," suggested Ben. "That way I can keep an eye on you and make sure you get enough sleep to be fit for work in the morning."

After school that day, four excited children gathered in the den with their sleeping bags.

"This is a brilliant idea, Nathan," said Luke.

"Especially as we get to see Minty and the puppies again," said Bethany. "I bet they've really grown. Where are they?"

"They sleep in the house now, ever since the night we thought Cheeky had been stolen," Nathan explained. "It's just as well though, or there would be no room in the den for us!"

"Let's go and find them," Rosie suggested.

The children spent the next hour playing with the puppies, then helping Mr and Mrs Howard prepare beef burgers and hot dogs for supper. There

was also Ben's tent to pitch and the camp beds and sleeping bags to arrange in the den. By the time this was done, it was evening and they were glad to relax on a rug outside the den and chat with each other.

"Remember all those jobs we thought about doing?" said Nathan. "We've done most of them now, and have got almost enough money to go on the school holiday. God has really helped us."

"You've done well," Ben agreed. "I know God is pleased with the way you have worked hard and learned how to handle money well."

"It's all because you started teaching us about God's way to handle money," said Bethany, and there was quiet as they thought about the things they had learnt. The peace was disturbed by a snuffling sound next to Luke.

"It's Cheeky!" Luke laughed, picking up the puppy. "How did you get out here?"

"That puppy always finds a way to get into mischief," Ben shook his head with a smile.

"Who's up for a game?" asked Rosie suddenly, sitting up. "Guess who I'm pretending to be."

The children had great fun, playing games and laughing. Finally Ben said, "Come on you lot. It's time to get some sleep so we can sort this garden tomorrow."

"Can Cheeky sleep with me tonight?" Luke asked. "Please, Ben. He wants to be with us."

"Go on then," said Ben and then he looked at the others. "I know what you three are thinking. Yes, go and get the other puppies! But you'll have to bring Minty too. The puppies are too young to be separated from their mother all night."

Twenty minutes later, the four children had settled into their sleeping bags, each with a puppy curled up at their feet. Ben stood by the door.

"Off to sleep then," he said. "We have to get up early tomorrow to clear the garden."

"Will you tell us a story first?" asked Bethany.

"Just one," agreed Ben, sitting down in the doorway. Minty came and lay by him, with her head on his lap. "After we finish the garden tomorrow, we're going to learn what God says about work. So let me tell you a story about a man in the Bible who built a wall. Not just any wall, it was a wall around an entire city! His name was Nehemiah. He lived during a time when some of God's people were returning to the home town of Jerusalem after years of captivity in a faraway land. Nehemiah can teach us some things about work."

The friends curled up in their sleeping bags and listened carefully.

"Nehemiah worked for the king who captured Jerusalem. One day Nehemiah heard bad news. The wall around Jerusalem was torn down. Those who lived in the city were poor and could not get the materials to rebuild the wall. Because the city had no walls, their enemies could attack them any time they wanted."

"Nehemiah's heart was broken by this news. He longed to see Jerusalem become a safe city. He prayed for the Lord to allow him to go and help build the wall. After he had prayed for several months, he told the king about the broken wall in Jerusalem."

"God worked in the king's heart, and he agreed to let Nehemiah go. The king even gave him supplies to build the wall."

"Nehemiah was very thankful. After he made the long journey, he met with the people of Jerusalem to tell them about his plan to fix the wall. He explained that God had caused the king to let him come to rebuild the wall.

When he finished, the people said, 'let us build the wall.'"

"The people began to build the new wall. But their enemies heard about this and decided to stop their work. First they sent people to make fun of the workers. When this didn't stop them, they decided to kill the workers."

"But Nehemiah heard about their plan and was ready with a better plan. He told half of the workers to work on the wall, and he gave swords to the other half to protect them as they worked. Day and night the guards watched for the enemies' attack. Try as they might, the enemies could not stop Nehemiah and the workers from building the wall. After only fifty two days the wall was completed. God had really helped them."

As Ben finished his story, Rosie said sleepily, "That's what God is doing for us, isn't it? He's helping us so that we can go on the school holiday."

"That's right," said Ben. He stood up and looked at his group of workers. Bethany was nearly asleep already with Eve under her arm. Nathan and Rosie were curled up with the puppies at their feet.

Luke was the last one to speak. "Good night, Ben," he yawned, pulling Cheeky closer so that he could not escape again. "This worker is going to sleep so I can do more than everyone tomorrow!"

*   *   *   *

They were woken up early in the morning by Ben's face appearing in the doorway.

"Time to get up!" he called. "We've got lots to do today."

"It can't be morning already!" Luke groaned, burying his head in the sleeping bag. "Let me sleep a bit longer."

"Remember what you said last night," Ben grinned at him. "You were going to be my best worker today!"

Slowly, the four children climbed out of their sleeping bags and made their way into the house to prepare for the day. Mrs Howard was already in the kitchen preparing a big breakfast of scrambled eggs, toast and cereal. By the time they had eaten it, the friends felt much more ready to tackle the garden.

Mr Howard met them outside and handed them each a spade and a large plastic bag.

"If the garden is cleared by tea time, you'll definitely have earned your money," he promised. "And there'll be a special prize for the person who works the hardest."

"How will you know?" asked Rosie.

"I have my spies!" Mr Howard said with a smile. "Ben and I will be working too. We have lots of bushes to cut back."

They all set to work and, except for a few breaks for snacks and lunch, worked hard all day. It was late afternoon when they finally gathered on the patio to look at what they had accomplished.

"You've done really well!" said Ben to the children.

"I'm really impressed," agreed his dad. "You four can certainly work hard. This looks like a different garden now."

"About time too!" said Mrs Howard, coming out to join them.

"So which of us worked the hardest?" Luke was keen to know.

Mr Howard looked at them all then shook his head.

"I really can't say," he said with a chuckle. "I'll have to give all of you the prize."

*   *   *   *

He went into the house and came out with a big bag of chocolate bars, and money which he handed out.

"Well done everyone," said Ben. "Nehemiah would have been happy to have you working with him on the wall around Jerusalem. Let's go back to the den and talk about what God wants us to learn about work. And bring that bag of chocolate. Now will be a good time to share them!"

When they were settled in the den and munching on chocolate, Ben began. "Work is so important that *2 Thessalonians 3:10* says, '*If a man will not work, he shall not eat.*' You see, one of the reasons God knows you should work is because work helps you grow and builds your character. For example, while you were working in the garden, you were improving your skills, becoming more diligent and even helping your muscles to grow stronger."

"And don't my muscles know it!" said Nathan, pulling a face as he rubbed his arms.

Ben laughed. "Does it surprise you to learn that God plays a big part in our work?" he asked. "First, God gives each of us special skills and abilities. *Exodus 36:1* tells us, '*And every skilful person to whom the Lord has given skill.*'

"God has given each of you special talents. Bethany, you have a wonderful talent for music. Luke, you are a gifted footballer. It's not a matter of one person being better than someone else. It is simply a matter of having received different abilities."

"How else does God help us in our work?" Rosie asked.

"God is the one who gives success," answered Ben as he reached for his Bible. "Luke, read what *Genesis 39:2-3* says about Joseph."

Luke read, "*The Lord was with Joseph, so he became a successful man…his master saw that the Lord was with him and how the Lord caused all that he did to prosper in his hand (NASB).*"

"So God has been helping us as we have worked to get our money for the holiday," Nathan said.

"That's right, Nathan," Ben agreed. "And there is one other thing the Bible tells us. We should do our work for the Lord. *Whatever you do, do your work heartily, as for the Lord rather than for men…It is the Lord Christ whom you serve. (Colossians 3:23-24, NASB)*.

"Think about your attitude towards work or school. If you could see Jesus as your boss or teacher, would you have a better attitude or try to work harder? I know that sometimes when I forget I am working for Christ, I don't do as good a job," said Ben. "The Bible encourages hard work. Wise King Solomon wrote in *Ecclesiastes 9:10, Whatever your hand finds to do…do it with all your might (NASB).*"

Ben stood up and stretched.

"You certainly worked with all your might today and could use a good night's sleep," he smiled. "Come over on Thursday after school and I'll have something unusual to show you. You're going to meet some small creatures who are both hard workers and wise savers. And that will be the next lesson – learning what God says about saving."

Memorise a verse

Whatever you do, do your work heartily, as for the Lord rather than for men…It is the Lord Christ whom you serve (Colossians 3:23-24, NASB).

Answer these questions

1. God plays a role in your work. Look up *Genesis 39:2-5, Exodus 36:1-2* and *Psalm 75:6-7*. What do each of these verses tell you about how the Lord is involved in work?

Genesis 39:2-5

_____

_____

Exodus 36:1-2

_____

_____

Psalm 75:6-7

_____

_____

2. Do you think most people understand that the Lord is so involved in their work?

_____

_____

3. Read *Proverbs 6:6-11* and *2 Thessalonians 3:7-10*. What do these verses say about working hard?

Proverbs 6:6-11

_____

_____

2 Thessalonians 3:7-10

_____

_____

4. Do you work hard at home and school? If you don't, what will you do to change?

_____

_____

5. Carefully study *Colossians 3:22-25*. Who do you really work for? Now that you understand this truth, how will it change your work habits?

_____

_____

Work it out

Think about some jobs that are done by eight-to-twelve year olds.

❑ Washing cars   ❑ Household jobs
❑ Garden jobs   ❑ Washing the dishes
❑ Looking after pets   ❑ Walking dogs

Write down a list of jobs you could do to earn money. Jobs I might be able to do:

1. _____
2. _____
3. _____
4. _____
5. _____
6. _____

What do you think you should say and how should you act and dress when you ask for a job?

_____

_____

_____

Write your prayer here

_____

_____

_____

_____

Studying with a group
Get ready for the next chapter

Read chapter 9, memorise *Proverbs 21:20* and answer the questions on pages 71 and 72, then complete the *Work It Out* exercise.

The ant farm

When the four friends arrived at Nathan's house on Thursday, Ben was already waiting for them in the garden. A large, thin box with one glass side was on the patio table. Ben was staring intently into it.

"Come on, you four!" he turned when he heard them come through the gate. "Have a look at this!"

"What is it, Ben?" asked Nathan, as the four children gathered around the table.

"An ant farm!" grinned Ben.

"An ant farm!" Luke and Rosie exclaimed at the same time.

"Where did you get it from?" Nathan wanted to know.

"And why have you brought it to show us?" asked Bethany.

"Slow down!" Ben laughed, standing up straight. "One question at a time! I got it from one of my friends, Len."

"Is he the strange one who rides a motorbike?" Nathan asked.

"That's the one," Ben nodded. "Though he's actually a great guy. He's just interested in some…well…different things!"

"This is certainly different!" agreed Luke.

"I wanted to show you," Ben continued. "Ants can teach us a lot about saving. Have a look at what they're doing."

They all watched as the ants scurried up and down little tunnels leading from the top of the dirt in the box all the way to the bottom. Several rounded out little 'rooms' could be seen.

Ben explained. "The ants feed the queen, take care of her babies, look for food and build the tunnels. The queen stays in her room making eggs for new ants."

"Look at the way they carry the bread crumbs from the top of the ground down into the little rooms below," said Rosie. "They save a lot of food, don't they?"

"Yes," Ben answered. "Some food will be eaten right away, but some food they save to eat another day."

They stood watching the busy ants for a few more minutes.

"Come and sit on the grass," said Ben, "and I'll read you what the Bible says about ants."

Ben found his place in the Bible while the four friends settled on the grass.

"We couldn't have sat here before last weekend," Bethany commented. "The grass was too long!"

"You're right, Bethany," Ben smiled. "You were as busy as those ants on Saturday, clearing the garden. Here we go, *Proverbs 30:24,25* says *"Four things on earth are small, yet they are extremely wise: ants are creatures of little strength, yet they store up their food in the summer."*

"They do that so they will have food to eat during winter when they can't find any food on the ground, right, Ben?" Nathan asked.

"That's right. And just like those ants who plan ahead, we should save too. But instead of food we need to save some of our money each time we receive it. *Proverbs 21:20* says, *The wise have wealth and luxury, but fools spend whatever they get (NLT)*. When we save we will have money when we need to buy something in the future. It also helps us stay out of debt."

"It's a good time for each of you to open a savings account. Then when you receive money, you can save some of it," Ben continued. "When you put your money into a savings account it actually grows, and you end up with more money than you put in. This extra money is called interest. Every month that you leave your money in the account, the savings company adds interest to the total that you have.

The longer you leave your money in the account, the more interest you earn."

"And if you are always faithful to save, your savings and the interest that you earn can grow into a lot of money. Wise King Solomon wrote, *the plans of the diligent lead to profit (Proverbs 21:5)*. 'Diligence' means to be persistent in doing something, that is, doing it over and over again. If you become a regular saver, the amount of money you have will grow to become large."

"But, Ben," said Luke. "I've seen adverts on television that said if I gambled, played gaming or the lottery, I could become rich. Is that true?"

"Good question, Luke," answered Ben, shaking his head. "A lot of people gamble or game, and many of them do it to make money fast without having to work. This does not please God. Unfortunately, most people lose money when they gamble or play gaming. My friend Len, who we talked about before, decided he didn't want to get a job this year but tried to raise his money for university by making bets and gambling. He lost everything and now he can't start university in September with the rest of us."

"That's awful," exclaimed Rosie. "I bet he's really mad about it."

"Fortunately he's started to listen to good advice now and got a job," said Ben. "He should be able to start university next year. But he's wasted a whole year of his life. And for many people it's a lot worse. Len has stopped gambling now, but a lot of people can't stop once they start. Some of them even gamble away the money that's needed to buy food for their family. Susie and I have decided it's best never to gamble – not even a penny."

"Saving is a lot wiser than gambling, isn't it, Ben?" said Bethany.

"You're right there, Bethany," replied Ben. "The Bible tells us about a young man who saved a whole country from starving because he learned how to save."

"The man's name was Joseph. He came from a big family of eleven brothers. Joseph was his father's favourite son. His father made a beautiful, colourful coat for Joseph. Joseph's brothers became so jealous of him they decided to get rid of him. So they stripped off his coat, threw him into a pit, and left him to die. But later they sold him to some people travelling to Egypt. To cover up what they had done, the brothers tore Joseph's coat and told their father that he had been killed by a wild animal."

"When Joseph arrived in Egypt, he was sold as a slave to one of the men who worked for Pharaoh, the king. Later, this man's wife lied about Joseph and he was thrown in prison. He stayed in prison for seven long years."

"One day Pharaoh had a disturbing dream, but no one could tell him the meaning of it. One of Pharaoh's men who had been in prison with Joseph remembered that he had interpreted his dream, and so they sent for Joseph to interpret Pharaoh's dream."

"With God's help, Joseph was able to interpret Pharaoh's dream. The dream told about seven years when there would be plenty of food in Egypt. At the end of seven years, a famine would begin and this would last for seven more years, during which there would be no food."

"Pharaoh was so thankful to Joseph for interpreting his dream that he made him the ruler over the land of Egypt."

"Joseph ordered everyone to save and store some of their food in Pharaoh's buildings so there would be enough food during the famine. When the famine began, he started to sell the food to feed the people during the time when no food would grow."

"The terrible famine spread to all the nearby countries. Weak and starving, Joseph's brothers came to Egypt for food. Joseph recognised them at once, but they did not recognise him. He sold them food, and later told them who he was. His brothers were shocked to see him, and were sorry for what they had done. Joseph forgave his brothers and asked them to bring his father and their families to Egypt to live."

The children had listened carefully to Ben's story, but now Luke interrupted. "I wouldn't forgive them. They threw him in a pit and tried to kill him. I would let them starve."

"Joseph never forgot what his brothers did to him," Ben said. "But he also never forgot how God had taken care of him and allowed him to become a great ruler. He forgave his brothers because he loved them, and because he knew God had sent him to Egypt to save his family's lives."

"But they really hurt him," said Rosie, with tears in her eyes. "It's hard to forgive people that really hurt you."

Ben looked at each child. "That's true, Rosie. It is hard. But Joseph is a picture of someone else in the Bible who was hurt deeply by the people He loved."

"You mean Jesus, don't you?" Bethany said softly.

"Yes, Bethany," Ben continued. "God loves us. In fact, He loves us so much that He sent His only Son, Jesus, to earth to die for us. *John 3:16* says, *For God so loved the world that He gave His only begotten Son, that whoever believes in Him should not perish, but have eternal life.*"

"God wants us to know Him and become part of His wonderful family. Unfortunately, each of us is separated from God because of sin. God is holy – which means He is perfect. But all of us have sinned, or done wrong things, like disobeying our parents or speaking unkindly to someone. *Romans 3:23* reads, *For all have sinned and fall short of the glory of God.*"

"Jesus came to die, be buried and rise back to life again so He could take away our sins. He did this so we could become part of God's family. Jesus said, '*I am the way, and the truth, and the life; no one comes to the Father, except through Me*' *(John 14:6)*. Jesus is the only way to heaven."

"We all need to ask Jesus to come into our life. When we do that, God will forgive our sins and give us the gift of eternal life, which is the best kind of life now and forever. It's the most important thing you will ever do."

"I asked Jesus to be my Saviour and take away my sin one Sunday at church," said Nathan.

"I've done that too," said Bethany. "My dad and mum told me about Jesus and prayed with me and I asked Jesus into my heart."

"Ben," said Luke quietly, looking down at the grass. "I've never asked Jesus to come into my heart and forgive me for the wrong things that I've done. What do I need to do?"

"Me neither," added Rosie. "How can I come to Jesus?"

"All you need to do is pray," said Ben. "In fact, let's pray right now. All of you close your eyes and repeat the words I pray."

They closed their eyes and prayed. "Dear Father God, thank You for sending Your Son, Jesus Christ, to die on the cross for my sins. Thank you for loving me so much. Please forgive my sin and come into my life. Thank you forgiving me. Amen."

There was quiet for a few minutes before Rosie spoke. "Ben, thank you so much for introducing Luke and me to Jesus. What do we need to do now?"

"You need to pray and read your Bible every day," Ben smiled. "You've made a good start over these last few weeks with me but you must keep going yourselves at home. It will help you to get to know Jesus better."

"And you can come to church with us," Nathan added. "That's a good place to find out more about Jesus too and to meet other Christians who can help you."

"It will be brilliant to all go to church together!" Bethany exclaimed, squeezing Rosie's arm. "This has been a really special day."

"But Ben," Luke suddenly had a thought. "Now I want God to answer our prayer and bring someone to us who we can give to. When is God going to answer that prayer?"

"I don't know exactly when, Luke," answered Ben. "But I have a feeling it won't be too much longer." He stood up and stretched. "Now don't forget all of you, on Saturday we're going to be working at Pinewoods again. And Susie's invited a special friend to join us. I think you're all going to get on great with her."

Memorise a verse

The wise have wealth and luxury, but fools spend whatever they get (Proverbs 21:20, NLT).

Answer these questions

1. Look up *Genesis 41:34-36* and *Proverbs 30:24-25*. What do you think these passages say about saving?

_____
_____
_____

2. How will you begin to save if you are not yet saving yet?

_____
_____
_____

3. If you have put money into a savings account, you will receive *interest*. How would you describe what *interest* is?

_____
_____
_____

4. Read *Proverbs 21:5*. According to this verse what is the benefit of saving regularly?

_____
_____
_____

5. How would you describe *gambling* or *gaming*?

_____
_____
_____

6. What are some of the different ways people gamble?

_____
_____
_____

7. Why do you think most people game, gamble?

_____

_____

_____

8. Do you think gaming and gambling displeases the Lord? Why?

_____

_____

_____

Work it out

If you do not have a savings account, discuss with someone who looks after you about opening one. Ask the person who opens the account how much interest they will pay you on your savings. Write down the interest rate you will be paid_____%

Did you ask Jesus to come into your life and forgive your sins? If you did, be sure to tell your teacher, parents/carers so they can help you grow to know the Lord better.

Write your prayer here

_____

_____

_____

_____

_____

Studying with a group
Get ready for the next chapter

Read chapter 10, memorise *1 Timothy 4:12* and answer the questions on page 79, then complete the *Work It Out* exercise on page 80.

A new friend

It was already sunny and warm when Rosie's dad dropped her off at Pinewoods early on Saturday morning. Rosie waved to her dad as he drove away then stood outside for a few minutes, looking at the blue, cloudless sky above her and enjoying the songs of the birds living in the nearby wood.

'Everything has seemed better and brighter since Thursday,' she thought to herself. 'I'm so glad Ben introduced me to Jesus.'

She was pulled away from her thoughts by Bethany's voice, and turned to see her friend coming out of the Pinewoods entrance.

"I thought I saw you arrive, Rosie," Bethany called. "We've been waiting for you. Guess what? There are two new horses here. They only arrived yesterday. Come and see!"

The girls ran inside and joined Nathan, Luke and Ben in the entrance. Susie came out of the office.

"Hi Rosie," she smiled. "Are you all ready to meet the new members of the Pinewoods family?"

"You bet!" said Luke and the others nodded excitedly.

Susie led them out to the stables. "You'll need to stay calm," she warned the children. "The horses are still settling into their new home. They are tame though, so they should get used to you quickly."

As the children approached the stables, a large reddish-brown coloured head appeared over the first door.

"Hello Chestnut, old girl," Susie said, stroking the horse's nose gently. "Have you come to see your new friends?"

"She's beautiful," said Bethany, reaching up her arm to stroke Chestnut's broad back.

"The other horse is shy," Nathan commented, looking into the next stable.

"He's younger," Susie explained. "So he's not quite so brave. Look, here he comes!"

The horse walked over to the door and stood still, as if checking them out. He was smaller but looked more active, and was black with a single white streak down his face.

"I like this one!" said Luke. "He looks as though he could gallop really fast."

"He used to be a racing horse," said Susie. "But now one of his legs is slightly lame, which is why he has come to us. His name is Flash."

"Good morning everyone," Mr Brent said as he came up behind them. "Are you welcoming our new arrivals?"

"They're great," Rosie said and the others agreed. "Could we ride them one day?"

"That's the plan," he nodded. "They'll need a bit longer to get settled, but you can be the first to try them out once I know they can be trusted with children. Is that a deal?"

"Yes!" the four friends all said together.

"Off to work then," said Mr Brent with a laugh.

"We'll have a picnic lunch outside later," Ben told the children as they separated to do their assigned jobs. "Then we can have our next lesson at the same time. See you all later!"

*   *   *   *

Several hours later, the children and Ben sat around a picnic table with empty lunch boxes in front of them.

"I was ready for that!" Ben said. "Working at Pinewoods always makes me really hungry."

The children agreed with a laugh. Then Bethany remembered something.

"Ben, you told us on Thursday that Susie had invited a special friend to join us today. Who is it and when are they coming?" she asked.

"Susie said they should be here after lunch, so you'll find out who it is very soon," Ben replied. "But first I want to tell you what God says about friends."

"Is that our next lesson?" asked Luke eagerly.

Ben nodded. "Do you know that God said that choosing the right kind of close friends is important? Close friends either encourage or discourage our life as a Christian. Rosie, read *1 Corinthians 15:33* and tell us what you think it means."

Rosie read, *"Do not be deceived: bad company corrupts good morals*. I think it says that if we are always with those who do bad things, we'll end up doing bad things too*."* *(NASB)*

"You're right, Rosie," said Ben. "It's important for us to have close friends who know God. This helps to protect us. They will encourage us to do the right things. So remember to choose your friends carefully."

"However, God does not want us to stay away from everyone who does not know Him. In fact, we should be an example to them. You're never too young to be an example. *1 Timothy 4:12* says it this way: *Don't let anyone look down on you because you are young, but set an example for the believers in speech, in life, in love, in faith and in purity*. There are people around you all the time who are watching you. This is especially true when it comes to handling money. When you handle money God's way, you are showing others how it can be done."

"But won't being careful about who we choose as friends be like having favourites and leaving people out?" asked Nathan with a frown.

"Nathan, that's a good question," answered Ben. "Carefully choosing friends because they are good is not the same as having favourites. Another word for having favourites is partiality. This is something God does not want us to do. Nathan, why don't you read *James 2:1* and verse *9* for us?"

Nathan read, *"Don't show favouritism.* That's pretty clear. It tells us not to show favouritism."

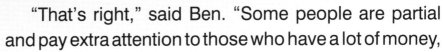

"That's right," said Ben. "Some people are partial and pay extra attention to those who have a lot of money, are popular or may be good looking. But a person who has favourites will not treat someone who is poor or unpopular that same way as they treat their friends. God want us to love all people."

"I know I only want to play with some children sometimes, and leave others out," Bethany admitted with flushed cheeks, and Rosie nodded too. "How can I stop doing that?"

Ben answered, "*Romans 12:10* tells us, *Be devoted to one another in brotherly love; honour one another above yourselves.* And *Philippians 2:3* reads, *In humility consider others better than yourselves.* These verses mean that we need to ask God to help us to think of each person as more important than ourselves."

"Try to think about the strengths and abilities of each person you know. Everyone can do some things better than we can. Keeping this in mind will help you appreciate all people. It will make you a better example of living your life God's way."

Ben looked up as Susie came towards them. With her was a woman pushing a wheelchair. Inside the wheelchair sat a girl with red hair, who looked a similar age to the four children.

As they reached the picnic table, Susie said, "Here's the visitor we've been waiting for! This is Mrs Frank and her daughter, Rachel."

"Hi everyone," smiled Mrs Frank.

The children greeted her then turned to Rachel. As she met each of them, her blue eyes lit up and she smiled warmly.

"Why don't you take Rachel to the stables and show her the new horses?" suggested Susie.

Rachel nodded eagerly.

"Nathan and I can push the wheelchair," Luke volunteered.

The children left the picnic area, speaking over each other in their eagerness to get to know Rachel and tell her about the horses. Rachel responded and soon they were laughing and talking like old friends. When they reached the stables, they were thrilled to find that Chestnut and Flash were out in the yard, being groomed by two of Mr Brent's workers. It was more than an half an hour later before they returned to find Mrs Frank, Susie and Ben.

As they approached, Susie said, "Well, Rachel, did you enjoy meeting the horses?"

"They are wonderful," Rachel responded. "Chestnut kept coming over to me. She even nudged the back of my chair. I think she wanted to help Luke and Nathan push me."

She turned to her mother and asked, "Can I stay for the afternoon, mum? Please? I want to see the other animals that Bethany and Rosie have been telling me about."

"Please, Mrs Frank," Rosie joined in. "She can help us do our jobs too."

"And maybe one day Rachel can come and see our den and meet Minty and her puppies. She could be with us while Ben teaches us about money," Nathan added. "That would be great!"

"About money?" exclaimed Mrs Frank. "I would like to learn more about money. Maybe Rachel could learn some things that would help me."

"God wants us all to know how to handle money," said Ben with a smile. "Would it be alright if Rachel stays this afternoon? I'll keep an eye on her for you."

"That's fine by me," agreed Mrs Frank and Rachel clapped in excitement. "I'll stay out here and catch up with Susie for a bit."

"Mrs Frank used to teach me music a few years ago," Susie explained. "That's how I got to know her and Rachel. Off you go then! See you later."

The children had a lot of fun with Rachel, and the afternoon seemed to fly past. It was getting late when they finally returned to the entrance, where Mrs Frank was waiting.

"Well Rachel," smiled Ben. "It seems like you've really enjoyed your visit here with this noisy bunch!"

"Oh, I did," Rachel said. "I can't remember when I last had so much fun!"

"Rachel, you fit right in with us," Bethany said. "It seems as though you have always been here."

"Yes," agreed Nathan. "You helped us a lot by measuring the feed for the animals into buckets while we cleaned the pens. We finished the jobs much faster."

"And the animals liked you," Rosie added. "Especially Chestnut!"

Ben smiled and said, "It's like God has brought Rachel into our lives, isn't it, guys?"

They looked at Ben and then at each other. They all nodded as Luke said, "Rachel, you're God's answer to our prayer. We didn't realise it until now."

"What prayer?" asked Rachel. "What do you mean?"

Ben spoke up quickly. "We've been praying for a new friend. And God sent you as an answer to that prayer."

"Mrs Frank," Bethany turned to Rachel's mother. "Will Rachel ever be able to walk again?"

"We hope so," replied Mrs Frank. "Rachel needs surgery which we have to travel abroad for. After that, she should be able to walk again."

"When will she have the surgery?" asked Nathan.

"As soon as we can afford it," Mrs Frank said. "It could do with being soon though, as Rachel is often in a lot in pain."

The children were quiet, not liking the idea of their new friend suffering. They cheered up a little as they arranged for her to meet them at Nathan's house the following weekend, before waving goodbye.

"We need to pray that Rachel can have the surgery soon," said Luke and the others agreed. "God has answered one prayer for us already today."

"Speaking of answers to prayer," Ben said. "You have two more weeks until you hand in the money for the holiday. Bring the boxes of money you have saved to the den next Saturday and we'll see if you have enough money for the holiday before Rachel arrives."

"I've got some more money to collect this week for jobs I've done," said Nathan excitedly. "I can't wait to find out if we can go!"

"Me too!" the other three shouted together.

Ben laughed. "And guys, I think that before you leave for this holiday, you'll discover God's secret for handling money."

Memorise a verse

Don't let anyone look down on you because you are young but set an example for the believers in speech, in life, in faith and in purity (1 Timothy 4:12).

Answer these questions

1. According to *1 Corinthians 15:33*, do our friends influence us? Why do you think it is important to have godly friends?

_____

2. How can your friends help you handle money wisely?

_____

_____

3. Read *1 Timothy 4:12*. What does this verse say about how you should be an example?

_____

_____

4. What are some of the ways you can be an example in handling money in a way that pleases the Lord?

_____

5. Look up the word partiality in the dictionary. Write down what you think it means.

_____

_____

6. Read *Leviticus 19:15* and *James 2:1-9*. What do these passages say about partiality (having favourites)?

Leviticus 19:15

_____

James 2:1-9

_____

7. Do you choose friends because they have a lot of money, are popular or are good looking?

_____

8. Look up *Romans 12:16* and *Philippians 2:3*. How do you think these verses will help you overcome partiality?

_____

Work it out

Think of some ways you can become a wise spender.
Read these spending tips:

- Don't carry any more money with you than you need. If you don't have money in your pocket, you won't spend it.

- When eating out, drink water and have dessert at home

- Designer clothing is expensive – avoid buying it!

- All pets cost money. Limit pets to those you really enjoy and can afford.

- Buying over the internet – compare prices and always keep to what you have decided to buy.

- Give and save first, before you spend, put your savings away as soon as you get your money…that way you'll always save more.

Now write down some ways you will spend more wisely:

1. _____
   _____

2. _____
   _____

3. _____
   _____

4. _____
   _____

Write your prayer here

_____
_____
_____
_____
_____
_____

Studying with a group
Get ready for the next chapter

Read chapter 11, memorise *Philippians 4:11-12* and answer the questions on pages 85 and 86, then complete the *Work It Out* exercise.

How much is in the boxes?

The children were excited and a little nervous as they gathered in the den on Saturday morning.

"I didn't sleep much last night," Nathan told the others. "I hope we have enough money to go on holiday."

"I've wanted to count the money in my box all week," Rosie admitted. "But it will be better to find out together."

"We have to be able to go, we just have to!" Bethany said.

Ben walked into the den. "Morning everyone," he said. "Let's look at our next lesson first then you can count the money in your boxes."

"Do we have to wait?" Luke groaned.

"It's not going to take long," Ben smiled. "You may well be too excited after to take anything in!"

"I do hope so," said Rosie longingly, as they all put their money boxes down and took out their Bibles.

Ben looked at them. "Bethany, do you know what contentment means?" he asked.

"I think it means being satisfied or happy with what you have," said Bethany.

"That's good Bethany," Ben nodded. "God wants us to be content with what we have no matter what happens to us."

"Today you're going to find out if you have enough money to go on holiday. But what if you don't? Do you think you could be content if you can't go?"

"That would be impossible for me," said Nathan, shaking his head.

"I understand how you feel, Nathan," Ben continued. "But let's look at the apostle Paul. Many difficult things happened to him. Listen to what he said. *[I was] beaten times without number, often in danger of death. Five times I received…thirty-nine lashes. Three times I was beaten with rods, once I was stoned, three times I was shipwrecked…I have been in labour and hardship, through many sleepless nights, in hunger and thirst, often without food (2 Corinthians 11:23-27, NASB).*"

"There's no way he could be content!" exclaimed Luke.

"Luke, I think you will be surprised," replied Ben. "Read what Paul said in *Philippians 4:11-13. I have learned to be content in whatever circumstances I am. I know how to get along with humble means, and I also know how to live in prosperity…I have learned the secret of being filled and going hungry, both of having abundance and suffering need. I can do all things through Him who strengthens me (NASB).*"

"Paul was content no matter what happened to him," Luke said in amazement. "He was content when he had a lot and when he had nothing. He was content when things were going well or when bad things happened."

"Rosie, can you guess where Paul was when he wrote this?" asked Ben.

"No," she answered. "Where was he?"

"He was in prison where he was chained to guards day and night," Ben replied. He paused then added, "And have you thought about Rachel?"

"What do you mean?" asked Nathan.

"Rachel has to stay in her wheelchair," Ben explained. "She can't run around and play like you four, and go wherever she wants to. Think about last Saturday; she couldn't do a lot of the things you did at Pinewoods. But did you hear her complain?"

"No," Bethany responded and the others shook their heads. "She kept saying how much fun everything was and how she was grateful to us for letting her join in."

"I think Rachel has learnt the secret of being content," Ben said.

"How can we become content?" Nathan asked.

Ben smiled and said, "There are several things you should know. First, you need to be faithful. And all of you have been faithful to work hard and save for the holiday."

"After you have been faithful, you can relax. You can be content because you can be sure God will do the best thing

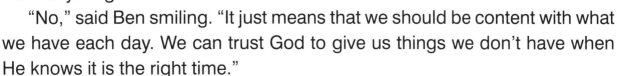

for you. Remember, God loves you. He knows what is best for you. God knows when it will be good for you to have something. He also knows when something might hurt your character, and stop you from being the best person that He has made you to be."

"Ben," Luke began, "does that mean we shouldn't want anything we don't have?"

"No," said Ben smiling. "It just means that we should be content with what we have each day. We can trust God to give us things we don't have when He knows it is the right time."

"Let me ask you all a question. What things cause you not to be content?"

"When my friends get new clothes, I'm not happy with mine anymore," said Bethany. "I want new ones too."

"I'm not content when I see some of the adverts on TV," admitted Nathan.

"Those are good examples," nodded Ben. "Television can be especially dangerous. The average young person spends 28 hours a week watching TV. They could see as many as half a million adverts by the age of 20."

"Have you ever taken a close look at adverts? Everyone seems so happy with what they are trying to sell you. Adverts often try to make you discontent. All they really want to do is get you to spend your money on what they are selling. Think about how much TV you watch. It could harm you more than you realise."

"I'd never thought about it like that before," said Rosie. "You're right, Ben."

"There's one more thing to talk about before you count the money," Ben continued. "And that is why we should take good care of our bodies. When you ask Jesus to become your Saviour, God's Holy Spirit comes to live in us. *1 Corinthians 3:16* says it this way: *Don't you know that you yourselves are God's temple and that God's Spirit lives in you?*"

"It's sad, but many kids start to hurt their bodies because they don't get enough sleep, they eat the wrong type of food or they don't exercise as they should. Some even drink alcohol, smoke or use drugs."

"We get enough exercise, don't we?" asked Luke.

"*You* certainly do playing football," replied Ben with a laugh. "And all of you have these last couple of months with the hard jobs you've been doing. You should exercise at least three times a week to keep your muscles strong and your body healthy."

"You also need to eat the right food. What would happen if we put water in a car instead of petrol? Do you think it would run well?" Ben asked. "Of course not! Your body works the same way. You need the right fuel to keep it running it well."

"What kinds of food should we eat?" asked Bethany.

"You need to eat a balanced diet of protein, vegetables and fruit. Don't eat too much junk food. And another thing to watch out for is sugar. It's often hidden in things like soft drinks, and too much is not good for you."

"If most people saved the money they spent on junk food and other unhealthy habits, they would be surprised at the amount of money they could save. I know because I've been doing it this year," Ben told them. "I've been amazed how much money I've been able to save but I've also felt a lot better as I've been eating the right things."

There was silence for a few seconds as the children took in what Ben had been telling them.

"OK everyone," Ben announced suddenly. "We've been talking about saving so get out your boxes. It's time to count the money!"

There was a flurry of activity in the den as the children found their money boxes then all was quiet as they nervously began counting. One by one, they found out they had enough. Luke was the last.

"We all have enough to go on holiday!" Luke shouted as soon as he had finished counting. "We're going on holiday!"

The four friends jumped up and began chanting "We're going to Wales! We're going to Wales!"

"It will be so much fun!" Rosie exclaimed, jumping up and down in excitement.

Ben clapped his hands. "Well done all of you!" he said. "You deserve to go. You worked very hard and were faithful to give and save."

"God answered our prayers," said Nathan. "He is so good."

"Yes, He is good," agreed Ben. "Come over next Sunday evening and we can have our last lesson before you hand your money in on Monday morning."

"Then it's less than one week 'til we go on holiday!" Bethany squealed. "In just a fortnight we'll be on our way!"

"And I think you're in for quite a surprise!" Ben commented with a a twinkle in his eye, but the children did not hear him in all of their excitement.

Memorise a verse

For I have learned to be content in whatever circumstances I am, I know how to get along with humble means, and I also know how to live in prosperity (Philippians 4:11-12, NASB).

Answer these questions

1. Look up the word *contentment* in the dictionary. Write down what you think it means.

_____

_____

_____

_____

2. What do *Luke 3:14*, *Philippians 4:11-12*, *1 Timothy 6:6-8* and *Hebrews13:5-6* have to say about contentment?

Luke 3:14

_____

_____

Philippians 4:11-12

_____

_____

1 Timothy 6:6-8

_____

_____

Hebrews 13:5-6

_____

_____

3. Write down some things that make you discontent.

_____

_____

_____

4. Read *1 Corinthians 3:16-17*. If you have asked Jesus Christ into your life, where does God live?

_____

_____

_____

5. Since you are a temple that God lives in, how should you take care of your body?

_____

_____

_____

Work it out

Learning to be content with what you have will help you become a wise spender. Think about these spending tips.

- Enjoy inexpensive hobbies and sport, like time with friends swimming and ball games. Try not to confuse shopping with fun.

- Pray before you buy anything. Ask the Lord if you really need what you want to buy.

- Don't watch too much TV or look at too many magazines. If you do, you'll spend more money.

Make a list below of all the junk food you eat this week. Write down some ways you could eat better.

Junk food	What I could eat that would be healthier for me

Write your prayer here

_____

_____

_____

_____

Studying with a group
Get ready for the next chapter

Read chapter 12, memorise *Mark 8:36* and answer the questions on page 92 and 93, then complete the *Work It Out* exercise.

The secret discovered

After tea on Sunday the children met in the den for the last time before the holiday.

"I still can't believe we're going to Wales on Saturday!" Luke exclaimed.

"Nor can I," said Rosie. "It's a dream come true."

"I've never seen four more excited children in my life," a voice behind them chuckled as Mr Kasanga came into the den with his wife and Ben. "Bethany could hardly sleep last night she was so excited."

"I was the same," Nathan told them. "I kept thinking of all the fun things we'd be doing next week."

"Do you know," said Bethany thoughtfully. "I've been on plenty of holidays before but none has meant as much to me as this one. I guess it's because I've worked hard to save the money myself."

Her mother smiled and gave her a hug. "We're proud of all of you," she said. "You've done really well."

"I hope you children don't mind, but we asked Ben if we could sit in on your last lesson," Mr Kasanga said. "We want to find out whether you have discovered God's secret of handling money."

"It will be a bit of a squash," laughed Ben, "but we'll manage!"

Once they were all squeezed into the den, Ben started. "There are two more things you should know about handling money God's way. The first is taxes. Rosie, do you know what taxes are?"

"Not exactly," said Rosie, shaking her head. "But my dad says he has to pay a lot of taxes. And he's not very happy about it."

"I can understand that," said Ben, smiling. "Taxes are what we pay the government so that it can do things for us, like build roads. As you get older, you will begin paying taxes."

"But do we have to pay taxes?" Luke asked.

"Someone asked Jesus the same question," replied Ben. "Turn to *Luke 20:24-25* and let's read what He answered. *'Show Me [a Roman coin]. Whose likeness and inscription does it have?' And they said, 'Caesar's.' And He said to them, 'Then render to Caesar the things that are Caesar's (NASB).'"*

"In other words," Ben said, "Jesus said to give to the government what is theirs. Many people try to avoid paying taxes. But that's not what God says. The Bible is clear about our responsibility to pay taxes that are due. *Let every person be in subjection to the governing authorities…for rulers are servants of God, devoting themselves to this very thing. Render to all what is due to them: tax to whom tax is due (Romans 13:1, 6-7, NASB).*"

"Ben, I understand about paying taxes," said Nathan. "What's the second thing you wanted us to know?"

"We should think about heaven when we spend money," replied Ben and stood up. "Come out here, everyone. I want to show you something."

They all followed Ben into the garden, where he had laid a long piece of rope on the grass, stretching from one end of the lawn to the other.

"Do you see this long line?" Ben pointed it out to the children.

"Yes, but what does it mean?" asked Bethany in a puzzled voice.

"This might be hard for you guys to believe," answered Ben, "but your life on earth is short. We will be spending eternity – forever and ever – with God in heaven, and when you compare that with how long we will live on earth, it is very short."

"Look over here," Ben bent down by the rope. "Right in the middle of this long line I put a penny. The little penny represents our time on earth. The long line represents the millions and millions of years we will be in heaven."

"And here is what's important to understand. How you spend your money during your life on earth will count forever. When you spend money in ways that please the Lord, He will reward you in heaven. You can either spend money helping others, or you can always spend selfishly on yourself."

"Remember what we learned in our first lesson. If we spend money God's way, we will grow closer to Him. Nothing in life is more precious than knowing God better. *Mark 8:36* says it this way, *What good is it for a man to gain the whole world, yet forfeit his soul?*"

"Wow!" Luke whistled. "That's given me lots to think about."

Just then, the garden gate opened and they all turned to see Susie walking over to join them. She looked upset.

"What is it Susie?" Ben asked, with a concerned look.

"Mrs Frank has just phoned me," Susie said. "Things aren't looking good for Rachel. Last night she was in so much pain that she couldn't sleep. She had to be rushed into hospital and the doctor says she needs an operation straight away. But they don't have enough money to pay for it. Mrs Frank is in such a state, she doesn't know what to do."

Bethany went over to stand by her. "Susie," she said, as tears filled her eyes. "I want Rachel to be able to walk. I think she was the answer to our prayer that God would give us somebody to help. But we haven't helped her with her biggest need. What can we do?"

"Let's ask God to show us what we can do to help," said Ben.

They bowed their heads. Each of them prayed, asking God to show them what they could do. As they finished, Nathan said quietly, "I know something we can do."

"What is it?" Luke asked.

"Rachel wants to walk more than anything else in the world. But she doesn't have enough money for her operation. We've saved a lot of money so that we could go on holiday. I don't know how much her operation costs, but I want to give her the money I saved so she can have her operation."

Immediately Rosie spoke up. "Nathan, that's a great idea. I wanted to go on this holiday more than anything else. But now I want to see Rachel walk more than I want to go to Wales. I want to give my money too."

"Me, too," said Bethany.

Luke's face was very serious. He stood quietly for a minute. Then he said, "I've never been on holiday before. I've been waiting for the time to come

for weeks. But since we met Rachel, the holiday doesn't seem as important. I think God wants me to give my money too. Going on holiday will have to wait."

Ben smiled and Mr Kasanga wiped a tear from his eye. His voice shook a little as he said, "You've done it! You've discovered the secret of God's way of handling money. Remember the verse you memorised from *Acts 20:35, "It is more blessed to give than to receive."* You found out it is true. It is more of a blessing for you to give to Rachel than to receive even something you wanted badly."

Mr Kasanga stopped and pulled a cheque book out of his pocket. "I'm going to keep my part of the deal now," he smiled. "I said that if you discovered the secret, I would pay half of your costs towards the holiday."

"But there's no point any more, dad," Bethany reminded him. "We don't have any money to pay the other half."

Mr Kasanga chuckled and looked at Ben. "Are you going to tell them, Ben?" he asked.

The four children looked at Ben with puzzled expressions on their faces.

"What is it, Ben?" Nathan asked.

"Now I have a surprise," Ben grinned. "During the last three months you have worked hard and studied hard to learn what God says about money. But today you have shown me that you're willing to sacrifice something you wanted very badly to help someone in need. Now you are about to receive a blessing."

He paused and pulled a leaflet out of his pocket. "Look where I'm going on Saturday," he said as he held up the leaflet for the children to see.

"But that's the Activity Centre in Wales where the school holiday is," said Rosie in a puzzled voice.

"What do you mean when you say that you're going there on Saturday?" asked Luke.

"Well," Ben smiled. "You know I'm doing lots of extra work to save money for university? One of the jobs I signed up for was helping out on activity holidays over the summer. I'm one of the team leaders on your school activity holiday! And I've just found out I can take four guests with me at half the cost. Since you gave your money to Rachel, do you fancy coming as my guests?"

The four friends couldn't believe their ears. They stared in amazement at Ben. Then they started shouting and hugging each other in joy. Mr and Mrs Kasanga, Susie and Ben laughed out loud at their excitement.

Finally, Susie said, "Shall we give Rachel a call and let her know the good news?"

"Yes!" they all shouted and dashed into the house. Luke stopped to say, "You know, Ben, it really does make me happy to give Rachel my money."

"Yes, Luke," Ben said as he put his arm around Luke's shoulder. "It really is more blessed to give than to receive."

*　　*　　*　　*

Six days later, Nathan, Luke, Bethany and Rosie met in the school car park with the rest of their friends, their bags packed and ready to go. Ben was there too, helping everyone to load their things onto the coach. They were just about to climb in to begin their journey to Wales when a car pulled up. Rachel was waving from the window.

"Rosie, Bethany, Nathan, Luke!" she called as they ran to the car. "I had to come and see you before you left." Her eyes were dancing with excitement. "Guess what?" she teased her friends.

"What is it, Rachel? Tell us," Rosie begged.

"By the time you come back from the holiday, I will have had my surgery," Rachel told them happily. "My doctor says that if everything goes well, I will be able to walk in just six weeks. I never could have had the operation if you hadn't helped me. I've never had any friends that meant as much to me as you."

Ben came up behind them. As Rachel finished, he said, "three months ago I would never have guessed that you would have learned so much about God's ways of handling money. I'm really proud of you. And I'm sure God is pleased, too."

Then he glanced towards the coach, where the other children were waiting to go. "Time to go," he said. "Let's go on holiday!"

"Thanks for everything!" Rachel called as they waved goodbye and ran to the coach.

Ben smiled as he jogged behind them. "Yes, God," he said quietly. "Thanks for everything!"

Memorise a verse

And what do you benefit if you gain the whole world but lose your own soul? (Mark 8:36)

Answer these questions

1. What are taxes?

_____

_____

_____

2. Read *Matthew* 22:17-21 and *Romans* 13:1-7. Do you think the Lord wants us to pay the government taxes that are due? Why?

_____

_____

_____

3. How would you describe *eternity*?

_____

_____

_____

4. Moses was rich when he was growing up. Read *Hebrews* 11:24-26. Why do you think Moses chose to suffer rather than to remain rich?

_____

_____

_____

_____

5. Do you think Moses is happy in heaven because he made this decision. Why?

_____

_____

_____

_____

6. Look up *Mark* 8:36. What do you think this verse means?

_____

_____

_____

7. Describe the most helpful part of this whole study.

_____

_____

_____

_____

_____

Work it out

Advertisers spend millions of pounds trying to get you to buy things. It is important to learn some of the tricks they use to get you to spend money.

Think about this. In most advertisements the people are smiling and seem so happy. In magazines they use pretty pictures. On TV they use music in ads to get you to buy what they are selling.

Now look at some advertisements. Write down how they try to get you to spend money.

What are they selling?   What tricks are they using in the advertisements?

_____   _____

_____   _____

_____   _____

_____   _____

_____   _____

_____   _____

Write your prayer here

_____

_____

_____

_____

_____

_____

Prayer records

"Pray for one another" James 5:16

Name: _____ Parents/carers: _____

Brothers and sisters: _____

_____

Week	Prayer requests	Answers to prayer
1		
2		
3		
4		
5		
6		
7		
8		
9		
10		
11		
12		

Prayer records

"Pray for one another" James 5:16

Name: _____ Parents/carers: _____

Brothers and sisters: _____

_____

Week	Prayer requests	Answers to prayer
1		
2		
3		
4		
5		
6		
7		
8		
9		
10		
11		
12		

Prayer records

"Pray for one another" James 5:16

Name: _____ Parents/carers: _____

Brothers and sisters: _____

_____

Week	Prayer requests	Answers to prayer
1		
2		
3		
4		
5		
6		
7		
8		
9		
10		
11		
12		

Prayer records

"Pray for one another" James 5:16

Name: _____ Parents/carers: _____

Brothers and sisters: _____

_____

Week	Prayer requests	Answers to prayer
1		
2		
3		
4		
5		
6		
7		
8		
9		
10		
11		
12		

Make your own money boxes
Giving, Saving and Spending

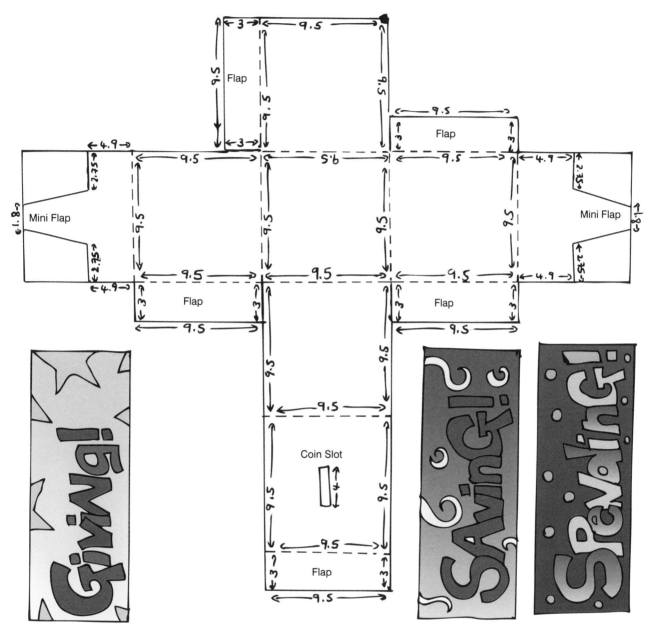

Your instructions:

Firstly note that this diagram is not to scale. Each measurement is in CM.

1. Draw the diagram – all measurements fit onto an A2 piece of card.
2. Cut out the diagram along the solid lines.
3. Fold along the dotted lines.
4. Place sellotape pieces along the flaps and stick them inside the box as it forms: the coin slot should be on top of the box and the two mini flaps should fit inside the slot.
5. Decorate the boxes with the labels above, or make your own.